ACTA UNIVERSITATIS GOTHOBURGENSIS

GOTHENBURG STUDIES IN ENGLISH 61

THE NEUROPSYCHOLOGICAL STATUS OF SWEDISH–ENGLISH SUBSIDIARY BILINGUALS

BY

GUNNAR BERGH

ACTA UNIVERSITATIS GOTHOBURGENSIS
GÖTEBORG SWEDEN

Except for typographical changes and a few minor corrections and additions, this book is identical with the author's doctoral thesis, with the same title.

Distributors:
ACTA UNIVERSITATIS GOTHOBURGENSIS
Box 5096
S-402 22 Göteborg

Minab, Surte 1986

Table of contents

II

Preface

The present thesis – my first _opus magnum_ – is the
fruit of some years' stimulating research done at the
English Department, University of Göteborg. During this
period, I have enjoyed generous support and assistance,
both theoretical and practical, from a number of students
and professionals in different fields, to whom I would
hereby like to express my gratitude.

Above all, thanks are due to Alvar Ellegård, who
originally drew my attention to and awakened my interest
in neuropsychological matters of language in general,
and bilingualism in particular. Apart from initiating
the basic experimentation reported here, he has served
as my principal mentor, and while allowing me great
freedom to pursue my own thoughts and theories, has never
failed to provide feed-back or further guidance when I
have needed it. Alvar Ellegård also made available to
me liberal grants from Humanistisk-Samhällsvetenskapliga
Forskningsrådet (HSFR), which have borne the costs of my
research throughout. I can only hope that what I have
achieved justifies the confidence bestowed upon me.

Further, I am indebted to Erland Hjelmquist and Ulf
Norrsell for undertaking the taxing work of proof-reading
preliminary drafts of the thesis. Their penetrating
comment and criticism from the specialist angles of
psychology and neurophysiology have no doubt saved me
from several embarrassing pitfalls. Likewise, I would
like to mention Aimo Seppänen and Mark Troy, who
unstintingly have read different versions of the manuscript and besides bringing, directly or indirectly, my
attention to various logical problems, also licked my
English into shape.

On the technical side, I have received valuable
experimental instruction and assistance from Per-Håkan
Ekberg (who tragically died in 1983). He also contrived
and procured the necessary test apparatus and, not least
important, lent me his personal computer. Ulf Dahlstrand
and Torbjörn Wikström have been equally helpful on
statistical matters. They adapted the experimental raw

IV

data for computer treatment and subjected it to various
in-depth statistical analyses. In addition, Ulf Dahlstrand
gave freely of his time to discuss with me any problems
that arose in this context.

Moreover, my obligation is due to the students at the
Burås Comprehensive School and the University of Göteborg
who willingly partook in my series of experiments. They
put in, often at short notice, an exacting 2 x 1.5 hours
each at what might not always have appeared as inspiring
test tasks, and without whose benevolent assistance, it
would never have been possible to carry through the present
project.

Finally, I would also like to thank my cohabitant,
Maria Carlberg, for assisting me in giving the thesis
its final edge and, not to be forgotten, for providing
consistent moral support during these years of inter-
mittent "brainstorming" and untimely lucubration.

Göteborg, December 1985

Gunnar Bergh

Abstract

Bergh, Gunnar. The Neuropsychological Status of Swedish-
English Subsidiary Bilinguals. University of Göteborg,
Department of English, 1986.

This monograph is a cross-sectional study of the neuropsychological language status in Swedish-English subsidiary
bilinguals - i.e. native speakers of Swedish with English
as a foreign language. Two aspects of brain organization
are dealt with - dual-language hemispheric lateralization
and functional interlingual dependence. The investigation
is designed to answer three major, interrelated questions:
What types of lateralization and interdependence patterns
obtain in the test population? What factors condition or
influence these patterns? What does variation in these
patterns consist of primarily - neurophysiological or
psychological change?

The methods of inquiry consist of four indirect, psycholinguistic experiments. Two are lateralization tests - a
dichotic listening task and a monotic (tachistoscopic)
viewing task - in which subjects' ability to recall
lexical material presented to the left and right ears
and visual fields respectively is studied. The results
are used to draw inferences about the relative participation of the two cerebral hemispheres in processing Swedish
and English words. Two are interdependence tests - two-
choice tasks of noun number and verb tense recognition
respectively - in which subjects' speed and accuracy of
inflectional identification are gauged. The response
data are related to a processing interference model,
the implications of which are used to determine the
extent of cross-language dependence between English and
Swedish morphological elements.

The test results show that Swedish-English subsidiary
bilinguals tend to organize their languages in a roughly
uniform and integrated manner in the brain. Both languages
exhibit left-hemisphere dominance and they show considerable interlingual dependence. When organizational
differences occur, they seem to be a function of subject

age/English proficiency level, age and manner of language acquisition, and cognitive ability. Two components of brain organization are discussed – a basic, neurophysio-logical substrate and a superordinate, psychological processing system. It is argued that the uniform, integrated representation of the languages is due to the static, genetically-derived character of the former, while the instances of variation are engendered by the developmentally and environmentally conditioned dynamics of the latter.

Key words: neuropsychology, bilinguals, psycholinguistic experiment, language lateralization, interlingual dependence, cerebral hemisphere, lexical interference, morphological interference, levels-of-processing, organizational component.

I. Introduction

What happens in the brain when a person becomes
bilingual? This seemingly plain and uncomplicated question
has inspired a great deal of research activity within the
fields of neuro- and psycholinguistics in recent years.
In particular, much attention has been devoted to the
intriguing problem of how two languages are processed and
stored in a single brain and what circumstantial factors
are of relevance in the course of this establishment. The
aim of such inquiries has typically been to explore and
describe the neurophysiological and/or psychological
consequences of second language acquisition by means of
finding systematic biological or behavioural effects in
the individual, which could help to disclose the as yet
rather recondite principles of bilingual language
organization.

There are two primary modes through which this issue
has been approached. On the one hand, studies have been
undertaken to chart the anatomical localization of the
bilinguals' underlying language representations in terms
of brain lateralization, i.e. by investigating the relative extent to which the two cerebral hemispheres
participate in processing each language (e.g. Albert &
Obler, 1978). Since it is generally acknowledged that the
left hemisphere is dominant for verbal processing in most
individuals (e.g. Bryden, 1982), the main concern has
been to determine the relation between the degrees of
left-hemisphere specialization that the languages exhibit.
On the other hand, there is the functional approach in
which the prime goal has been to map the neuropsychological
dependence relation that exists between the languages,
without any localizational aspirations (e.g. Lambert, 1969).
As the bilinguals' languages normally do not behave as
functionally self-contained linguistic units that operate
strictly independently, but rather as partly interdependent
systems (e.g. McCormack, 1977), the manner in and extent
to which they are interconnected in the brain have
constituted a natural point of scholarly attention.

Together, these approaches have yielded a large and

comprehensive body of empirical research data, from which
our knowledge of different neuropsychological mechanisms
and processes of bilingualism has benefited considerably.
Unfortunately, however, if seen in a larger perspective,
the material has often been too heterogeneous to be
integrable into a consistent general theoretical framework of how the bilingual brain is organized. The reason
for this is that various conflicting patterns of both
localizational and functional language disposition, with
shifting or only semi-regular relationships to different
circumstantial variables, have been observed or inferred
(cf. Paradis, 1977; Albert & Obler, 1978; Galloway, 1983).
Although no efforts seem to have been spared to resolve
this issue, there is thus still a great deal of uncertainty
as to the status of both the lateralization and dependence
relations between the first and the second language, and
also as to what factors determine the type and value of
these interlingual associations. In addition, the basis
of organizational variation along these parameters does
not appear to be sufficiently explored, since it frequently
remains unsettled whether recorded differences are
anatomically or physiologically represented or only
consist of differential psychological functioning and
cognitive approach. This ambiguous state of affairs
clearly calls for further research on the topic in order
that we may achieve a greater understanding of the
organizational processes that take place in the brain
when a person becomes bilingual. It is as a step towards
supplying this desideratum that the present thesis is
intended.

1. The present project

The following investigation will thus be concerned
with localizational and functional aspects of neuropsychological language organization in bilinguals. As
the term implies, we take the notion of organization in
a broad sense, meaning that the whole range of language-

relevant levels from basic cerebral representation to
subtle cognitive processes are included. However, in
order to maintain a reasonably clear distinction between
psychological and physiological effects, which is
heuristically important here, we will leave out considerations of physiological differentiation at the cell level.
This is because changes in the brain's apparently in-
finitely malleable cognitive functioning, for example
such that take place when different lexical items are
learnt, always seem to go hand in hand with certain
modifications of neural circuitry - i.e. synaptic
distribution and efficiency and cellular electrochemical
values in the substrate (cf. Ellegård, 1982). If we included microbiological aspects of organization, it would
not be meaningful to try to contrast psychological and
physiological processes against each other, since the one
usually presupposes the other. Instead, we will confine
ourselves to possible grosser and more conveniently
measured physiological effects in the cerebral cortex,
which are not necessarily, and not primarily, a reflection
of single language experiences, but rather of more general
linguistic processes and manifestations. Such effects
would consist of neuromorphological changes demonstrable
in, for example, CT scanning or angiographic tests,
in vivo aphasiological investigations, and post-mortem
anatomical studies.

In dealing with the notion of brain organization,
moreover, we will apply a quantitative perspective - i.e.
lateralization and interlingual dependence will be treated
as continua rather than as static two- or three-value
factors. In other words, our concept of organization
allows of in principle any degree of left- or right-
hemisphere dominance, including bilaterality, as well as
any degree of interrelation between the languages from
separation to identity. Although some important clinical
evidence has accommodated a binary view only (see e.g.
Bryden, 1982), quantification seems to be the generally
and justifiably employed approach (e.g. Corballis, 1983;
Riegel, 1968; Diller, 1974). The perhaps most forceful
defence of this position is that so functionally subtle

and flexible a mechanism as the human brain would hardly
develop or operate according to any simple binary or
tripartite deployment principles, but a correspondingly
complex and variable pattern of organization is rather
what one would expect.

Our aim here is to examine on an experimental basis
the mutability of the language correlates in the brain
in terms of hemispheric dominance and interlingual
connection, and to shed some light on what any changes
in such organization may consist of. The most plausible
and practicable way of achieving this seems to be to
determine the lateralization and interdependence patterns
of the languages, and identify and rank the importance of
different factors inherent in or parallel to the bilingual
state and its development that appear to condition these
patterns. The resulting picture may then be matched
against known or proposed anatomical-physiological and
psychological mechanisms and processes in the brain, from
which we may, hopefully, be able to construct a viable
model of how the languages are organized.

The first thing we have got to do in realizing this
undertaking is to stake off an appropriate and manageable
field of inquiry. It goes without saying that we cannot
bring up for examination the whole gamut of language
material, bilingual speakers, and investigation methods
in existence, but we have to delimit our endeavour to a
certain part or parts of the problem.

In short, then, the following selection of test
constituents was made. As our linguistic targets, we
decided upon Swedish and English. Since the experimentation was to take place in Sweden and there are a great
many Swedes who in addition to their native language
know English - learnt primarily at school - to different
extents, this was the most natural and practical choice.
This combination yielded the opportunity to study the
potential organizational influence of certain factors
that varied across the languages - for example, age and
manner of acquisition, but also structural similarity
as there are many both similar and dissimilar forms and
features between Swedish and English.

Moreover, the material was confined to the lexical and morphological domains of the languages. A division was made here in such a way that the localizational aim of our study was directed towards the lexical stratum and the functional aim towards the morphological. This distinction was conditioned by, on the one hand, the fact that the apparently only handy method for examination of language lateralization involves lexical material, and, on the other, the urge we felt to test our own newly devised method for studying functional interdependence within the morphological field. As the lexical and morphological strata theoretically constitute separate yet closely connected linguistic subsystems, we tried at the same time to create by this dual approach an equilibrium of broadness and unity concerning the scope of the selected test material, from which sufficiently reliable conclusions as to the mutual neuropsychological status of the languages in general could be drawn.

Regarding the test population, we had to collect an appropriate sample of Swedish-English bilinguals in order to meet the linguistic requirements just stated. A category which naturally suggests itself is Swedish students who are learning English at different levels within the educational system. Such individuals usually exhibit both qualitative and quantitative differences of competence between the languages, i.e. their knowledge of English is as a rule considerably below their knowledge of Swedish, and it tends to be more passive and metalinguistic as well - let us therefore call these school-learners subsidiary bilinguals henceforth. By selecting subjects at different stages of learning English, we may be able to test the possible organizational effects of the factors proficiency in English and subject age (which covary here). The choice of subsidiary bilinguals also has the advantages that subjects are easily accessible and that they tend to have fairly homogeneous language acquisition histories, which means that we can exercise some control of other important factors in this context.

The methods of investigation, finally, came to consist of two different types of experimental psycholinguistic

procedure. Both of these implicated receptive language
performance. On the localizational side, we developed
two variants of the common free recall task involving
laterally presented stimuli. These experiments - one
auditory and one visual - were devised in order to obtain
parallel measures of how Swedish and English lexical
processing are mutually lateralized in the brain. On the
functional side, there was a similar design with two
parallel experiments, but these consisted of reaction-
time tests of noun and verb form identification
respectively. By simple manipulation of the relation
between the inflections of English words and their
Swedish translation equivalents, we tried to compose
interference paradigms that might be able to shed some
light on how the underlying morphological subsystems are
neuropsychologically interconnected.

2. General plan

The contents of this thesis will be arranged in the
following way. In the next chapter (Chapter II), we
consider the localizational aspect of language organization in the bilingual brain by reporting and discussing
our two lateralization experiments. The functional aspect
of organization will thereafter be attended to in Chapter
III, in which our interdependence experiments will be
treated in a similar fashion. Then, to round things up,
we will devote Chapter IV to a brief discussion of the
general implications of the findings from the above
approaches. This will also include a synopsis of the most
important results arrived at.

II. Lateralization

The issue of hemispheric specialization of language in bilinguals has been subject to numerous investigations during the last century. From the rich body of literature on the topic, two main sources of evidence may be recognized, which, despite being indirect[1], have yielded a great deal of information on both the quality and quantity of dual language lateralization. The first refers to <u>clinical studies</u> of bilingual aphasic patients, who evince different types and degrees of language disturbance following brain damage. The second involves <u>experimental studies</u>[2] in terms of elaborate neuro- and psycholinguistic testing of neurologically intact bilinguals. Together, these approaches have been conducive to the identification of a set of <u>circumstantial factors</u> pertaining to different types of individuals, languages, and language acquisition histories, which are thought to influence bilingual lateralization patterns.

---

1. More direct sources of evidence are, for example, pharmacological (amytal) deactivation of one hemisphere (e.g. Rasmussen & Milner, 1977), unilateral hemispherectomy (e.g. Basser, 1962), and cerebral blood flow tests or CT scanning (e.g. Ingvar, 1983), but since these (neuro-physiological) tests have been performed almost exclusively on monolinguals or on one language in bilinguals only, we are confined to indirect neuropathological and psycho-logical observations here (cf. Norrsell, 1985).

2. The distinction between clinical and experimental studies is of course not a mutually exclusive one. On the contrary, there are a number of investigations which involve both clinical and experimental research aspects and which thus theoretically belong to both categories. (Studies of this type have in the main been included in the clinical section.) Nonetheless, we will use these terms here as they seem to adequately reflect the character of the two major approaches to the present field of inquiry.

1. Clinical studies

Until recently, <u>bilingual aphasia</u>, or <u>polyglot aphasia</u>, constituted virtually the only means for investigating language organization in the bilingual brain. The method typically involves scientific examination of the neuro-psychological relationship between the aphasic patient's languages, or the effects of dual language competence on such organization as compared to monolingual ability. The degree of localizational specification in these types of inquiry varies - some researchers have only been concerned with relative differences between the languages, referring to the brain as a whole, while others have been more specific, focusing either on inter- or intrahemispheric relations. Despite the danger of using neuropathological material when drawing inferences about healthy individuals[3], bilingual aphasia has proved to be an invaluable source of information in studies of the representation of two languages in one brain.

Aphasiological data have mostly been gathered through analyses of different patterns of impairment or loss of language ability following unilateral cerebral damage, or through observations of language recovery subsequent to aphasic incursion. When differential derangement or restitution has obtained, it has been interpreted as evidence for distinct representations of language in the brain, often in terms of differential hemispheric lateralization. Conversely, when the aphasic symptoms have been equally dispersed over the languages, common neuropsychological systems, or similar lateralization, have been postulated. In the vast majority of cases, substantial left-hemisphere dominance for the processing of both the bilingual's languages has been indicated. This is especially true for the expressive modalities (speech and writing), which have exhibited strong lateralization, whereas receptive functions (listening and

---

3. Cf. Hughlings Jackson who claimed many years ago that "to locate the damage which destroys speech and to locate speech are two different things" (in Taylor, 1958, p. 130).

reading), though being clearly left-lateralized, have displayed a more moderate asymmetry (e.g. Albert & Obler, 1978; Paradis, 1977; Gloning & Gloning, 1965). It is important to remember here that in those cases where no distinction is maintained between production and reception of language, the aphasiological data often show a predominance in favour of the expressive domain. Although, admittedly, both types of performance have been extensively studied, there is a quantitative preponderance for output disturbances, a development which seems rather natural in view of the inherent methodological difficulties that tend to accompany any measurement of perceptual and comprehension processes.

The incidence of bilingual language dissociation - i.e. cases where differential organization of the languages is indicated - has been subject to some dispute. In eclectic reviews of aphasic cases during the last century, Paradis (1977) and Albert & Obler (1978) reported unparallel impairment in 50-60% of the instances, findings which suggest that the languages are often distinctly represented in the brain. However, the high value of this figure should be treated with caution, since the data stem from a collection of selected cases, where the estimated frequency of occurrence probably is inflated due to a predilection on the part of previous researchers for unusual or clinically interesting cases, among them presumably such as exhibit differential language disturbances. In random case studies, on the other hand, i.e. where the instances of aphasia have been randomly chosen, a much lower rate has emerged. For example, Charlton (1964) found only two cases of language dissociation in the nine aphasic bilinguals he examined, L'Hermitte et al. (1966) reported none out of eight instances, and Nair & Virmani (1973) found only two out of 33 cases. According to this type of investigation, the incidence of differential organization is in the range of 10% only, and as random case studies are preferable from a statistical viewpoint, this measure is likely to mirror the true state of affairs more accurately. Support for such a low rate is also given by statements like that of Obler

(1981): "the norm is that both òr all languages are
impaired and recover in like manner, proportional to how
well they were known before the aphasia-producing accident"
(p. 2). Hence, the best clinical evidence available
indicates that language dissociation in bilinguals does
not obtain in the large majority of cases, but should
rather be viewed as an exceptional phenomenon.

Several aphasiological studies have also addressed the
issue of whether bilingualism has any overall effect on
hemispheric lateralization. In particular, it has been
proposed that bilinguals are more bilaterally organized in
the brain than monolinguals, with the right hemisphere
playing a more active role in language processing, since
it allegedly is specialized in second language acquisition
(e.g. Ovcharova et al., 1968; Vildomec, 1963). If this is
so, there should be a higher frequency of crossed aphasia
- i.e. dextrals suffering from aphasia through lesions in
the right hemisphere - in bilinguals as compared to monolinguals.

In fact, this is just what Galloway (1977) found in her
study of such groups of individuals - 86% of the bilingual
patients had become aphasic after damage to the left hemisphere, whereas the corresponding score for monolinguals
was 98%. Conversely, 14% of the bilinguals displayed
aphasic disturbances following damage to the right hemisphere, while only 2% of the monolinguals were affected by
lesions on this side. Similarly, Albert & Obler (1978)
reported that about 90% of their right-handers suffered
language disruption after damage to the left hemisphere,
whereas 10% evinced aphasia from right-hemisphere injuries,
figures which are to be compared with the authors' estimated
1-2% incidence of crossed aphasia in monolinguals. Both
these investigations consist of selected aphasic cases,
but comparable findings have also been recorded in random
case studies, for example Gloning & Gloning (1965).

Though most lateralization inquiries to date show a
tendency for the languages of bilinguals to be less
lateralized to the left hemisphere than those of monolinguals, the strength of the trend must not be exaggerated.
Rather, since the incidence of aphasia caused by lesions

in the right hemisphere amounted to `10-15% only, and the
remaining 85-90% of the cases obviously were engendered
by left-hemisphere trauma, the overwhelming proportion of
bilinguals examined still seem to be dependent on the left
hemisphere in a way similar to monolinguals, whether the
discussion is confined to the first (L1) or the second
language (L2), or refers to both. Just as was the case
with the incidence of differential language impairment,
bilaterality or right-hemisphere dominance of language
processing in the bilingual brain appears to constitute
a minor and rather infrequent deviation from the norm of
left-hemisphere dominance demonstrated in dextral bilinguals
and monolinguals alike.

However, in those cases where bilingual language
dissociation or enhanced bilaterality has been indicated,
we must seek its possible underlying causes. It is undeniable that some clinical assessments of this type of
language organization have been fragmentary and
impressionistic due to insufficient control of different
influential factors, and as a consequence, it often
remains an unresolved question whether the observed
effects are neuropsychologically real or only represent
an artifact of the examination procedure. A good start
for a greater understanding of these processes, therefore,
seems to be to tentatively identify the circumstantial
factors behind the bilingual state (see further Section 3
in this chapter).

2. Experimental studies

Whereas clinical studies of bilingualism have focused
on the relative dissociation of language in the brain and
the impact of language duality on cerebral organization
at large, experimental research has mostly been confined
to elaborate investigations of interhemispheric relations
between the languages of the bilingual. Specifically,
investigators have tried to assess the extent to which
the right hemisphere participates in L2-processing

relative to the left hemisphere and L1 respectively, and
what factors condition a potential laterality difference
between the languages. The studies have been carried out
using a variety of indirect test methods - primarily
lateral presentation of auditory and visual stimuli, but
also various electrocortical measures (EEGs etc.) and
different interference and reaction-time techniques, most
of which have been developed during the recent upsurge of
interest in the neuropsychology of language. These non-
invasive approaches have enabled researchers to examine
the bilingual brain in an intact state, where neither
damage nor medical manipulative treatment has disturbed
the natural physiology of the nervous system, and as a
consequence, the neuropsychological field has been
furnished with a new and intriguing perspective of the
brain-language issue.

   In contrast to aphasiological studies, which have
concentrated on problems of language production in a
broad sense, experimental work on non-aphasic bilinguals
has often been limited to receptive aspects of language
performance. In particular, there has - for methodological
reasons - been a focus on the lexical stratum. Left-right
perceptual and comprehension asymmetries and electro-
potential disparity recorded from different tests in this
realm have been taken as prima facie evidence for the
direction and extent of underlying cerebral lateralization,
giving rise to various subtle patterns of interhemispheric
organization in bilinguals. As expected, these results
have consistently indicated left-hemisphere dominance for
both languages, but within this left-sided preponderance,
a substantial variation in the relation between L1 and L2
has been noted. Three broad types of lateralization
pattern may be recognized: (1) L1>L2, i.e. L1 is more
lateralized than L2 (e.g. Maitre, 1974; Obler et al., 1975),
(2) L1=L2, i.e. L1 and L2 are equally lateralized (e.g.
Kershner & Jeng, 1972; Hamers & Lambert, 1977), and
(3) L1<L2, i.e. L1 is less lateralized than L2 (e.g. Rogers
et al., 1977; Wesche & Schneiderman, 1981). It is premature, however, to decide which of these alternatives
reflects the neuropsychological status of the average

bilingual most accurately, since, as implied earlier, there are many confounding circumstantial factors of potential relevance to bilingual hemispheric organizatioᶯ that need further examination (see Section 3 in this chapter).

A rough estimate of the incidence of left-hemisphere dominance in a cross-section of experimental lateralization studies on bilinguals indicates that about 70% of the tested individuals display this bias, while the remaining 30% show either a reversed pattern or hemispheric equivalence. At first sight, it is somewhat puzzling to find that the figures in favour of the left hemisphere are systematically about 20 per cent units lower than those calculated in clinical investigations (approximately 90%, cf. Galloway, 1977; Albert & Obler, 1978), but closer scrutiny of this apparent paradox suggests a plausible two-fold solution. First, some researchers have implied that in addition to the target effects, certain experimental methods may be measuring factors unrelated to the assessment of hemispheric specialization or that they may vary in their overall reliability, making it hard to achieve an accurate evaluation of the extent of language lateralization (Bryden, 1966; Blumstein et al., 1975). Such factors or inconsistencies, e.g. reading scan habits (Heron, 1957) or selective attention (Kinsbourne, 1970), seem however to be of a subsidiary nature, which in comparison with the influence of cerebral dominance assume a peripheral role at the most (cf. Levy, 1974). Second, and more importantly, a majority of clinical procedures involve parameters of language production, while experimental techniques tap primarily language perception, recognition, and comprehension processes. Previously, we have seen the necessity to distinguish between expressive and receptive language lateralization in the context of clinical cases, speech and writing exhibiting a higher degree of left-hemisphere specialization than listening and reading (cf. Zaidel, 1976; 1978), and in the light of these circumstances, the present lack of agreement between the two disciplines is what one may well expect. The ostensible underestimation on the part of the experimental findings would thus seem to be sufficiently accounted for by a combination of inherent difficulties associated with certain sensory test methods, and the fact that it is mainly language production that has been measured in clinical investigations, whereas language reception in a corresponding way has served as target in experimental studies.

The increasing number of experimental studies in brain research has also led to a partial revision of the concept of language lateralization in general. The traditional view derived from aphasiological studies, which emphasized stimulus characteristics - for example, type of word, morpheme, phoneme, or grapheme - as being directly responsible for recorded lateral asymmetries, has been challenged by an alternative explanation in terms of separate information-processing systems that are not immediately activated by the features of the stimuli. In this model, the intrinsic stimulus characteristics are not of paramount importance to selective hemispheric processing, but rather the way these features are utilized (Bever, 1975; Tomlinson-Keasey & Kelly, 1979). Hence, while stimulus quality per se is ascribed an indirect effect on lateralization, the crucial factor would be mode of processing in the respective hemispheres, where the left hemisphere is regarded as specialized in sequential, analytical, and propositional processing, and the right hemisphere in simultaneous, synthetic (Gestalt), and appositional processing (Levy-Agresti & Sperry, 1968; Bogen, 1969; Cohen, 1973). The lateralization patterns for different language functions, be it lexical or grammatical strata or language as a whole, would then vary more according to the mode of processing that a particular task requires than according to the immediate type of verbal stimulus and its strict neuroanatomical representation.

An important implication of this revised lateralization concept is that a view of more equipotential cerebral functioning has emerged, which transcends the previous strongly lop-sided model. Today, we tend to disregard the quantitative notions of a major (left) and a minor

(right) hemisphere, which once were in frequent use in
different clinically-derived theories (for a review, see
Dingwall & Whitaker, 1974), and instead, while recognizing
their equal working capacity, focus on qualitative
differences between the hemispheres. The current idea is
thus that both hemispheres participate complementarily
in language processing, but in different degrees depending
partly upon genetic language predisposition of the brain
and partly upon the psychological activity that verbal
material, modality, and task induce[4]. As linguistic
performance presupposes an aggregate of underlying
processes, some of which may be better handled by the
left hemisphere and others by the right, the typical
left-hemisphere dominance probably reflects to a greater
or lesser extent the prevailing analytically-based or
propositional character of language. (For a critique of
the analytic-holistic distinction, see Studdert-Kennedy,
1981.)

3. Factors conditioning cerebral lateralization

As appears from the preceding sections, both clinical
and experimental studies have given rise to a variety of
often conflicting theoretical models of the neuropsychological organization of language in bilinguals. In
order to appropriately interpret apparently contradictory
findings, it seems necessary to discuss a number of
factors that are of potential relevance to the present
issue. Hence, below, a brief, selective review will be

---

4. Recently, the view of hemispheric equipotentiality
has received strong support also from the clinical
field. Ingvar (1983), for example, using cerebral blood
flow tests (CT scanning) has shown that language
processing generally activates large areas in both
hemispheres (but still with a left-sided preponderance),
and that the distribution of this activity changes
systematically with different types of verbal performance.

given of factors suggested to contribute to different
patterns of lateralization in bilinguals. For the sake
of convenience, these may be grouped into individual-
specific, language-acquisitional, and language-specific
factors. It should be noted, however, that although for
clarity the factors are treated separately here, normally
no unitary, independent explanations have been put forward
in this context. This seems natural since the quality and
quantity of cerebral lateralization probably are dependent
on a complex, multidimensional interaction of many
different variables.

3.1. Individual-specific factors

Hand preference: It is reasonably clear that handedness
and cerebral lateralization for language are to some
extent correlated, although the correlation is not
perfect. As the physiological and evolutionary causes of
this relation have been discussed on numerous occasions
elsewhere (e.g. Lenneberg, 1967; Corballis, 1983), we
will leave them aside here and merely make some general
observations.

Since hand preference is easier to measure than
hemispheric dominance for language, it has generally
been taken as the primary parameter, to which different
patterns of hemispheric specialization have been coupled.
Thus, among monolinguals, it has been observed that the
incidence of left-hemisphere dominance in dextrals is
in the range of 95-100%, whereas sinistrals/ambidextrals
display left-dominance in 70-80% of the cases. The
remainder show either bilaterality or right-hemisphere
dominance (e.g. Zangwill, 1960; Milner, 1975; Carter et
al., 1980; cf. LeMay & Culebras, 1972).

For bilinguals, similar relations seem to hold. Although
few studies have explicitly investigated the influence of
handedness on bilingual lateralization, most of the
available data conform to the findings of monolingual
inquiries. Dextral bilinguals demonstrate as a rule left-

hemisphere dominance for both languages (e.g. Albert &
Obler, 1978; Walters & Zatorre, 1978; Gordon, 1980),
while sinistral/ambidextral bilinguals, as would be
expected, exhibit different or even conflicting patterns
occasionally. Unfortunately, there seem to exist only
two studies of sufficient reliability bearing on this
latter, non-dextral category - Gaziel et al. (1978)
found the left hemisphere to be dominant for both languages,
whereas Orbach (1967) obtained a crossed relation, with
right-hemisphere dominance for L1 and left-hemisphere
dominance for L2.

Familial handedness: It has also been proposed that
the hand preference of one's family members is of relevance
in this context. Specifically, the extent of familial
sinistrality - i.e. parents or siblings who are left-
handed - is thought to influence cerebral organization,
there being a greater likelihood for individuals irrespective of handedness to evince less left-hemisphere
dominance, bilaterality, or even right-hemisphere dominance
in case of familial left-handedness (e.g. Zurif & Bryden,
1969; Hécaen et al., 1981; Lake & Bryden, 1976). Though
most of these investigations have been carried out on
monolinguals, there are a smattering of studies yielding
similar indications for bilingual populations. Gaziel et
al. (1978), for example, found that dextral bilinguals
with familial sinistrals showed less pronounced left-
hemisphere dominance for their languages than corresponding
subjects with no such family members, and analogous
findings have also been reported by Shimizu & Endo (1981).

Sex: Subject sex is another possible conditioner of
language lateralization. When a difference has been
recorded over this variable, it has as a rule been in
terms of lower laterality in females than in males (e.g.
Lansdell, 1962; McGlone, 1980; Kimura, 1983). In
particular, females are thought to be vested with more
bilateral comprehension abilities, while in expressive
organization, equal laterality between the sexes is
postulated (Milner, 1975). This effect has been explained

in different ways - either as coupled to natural
biological development (e.g. Waber, 1977; Witelson, 1977),
to certain social-psychological conditions (e.g. Maccoby &
Jacklin, 1974; Fairweather, 1976), or induced by differential
cognitive strategies (e.g. Bryden, 1980).

It is far from clear, however, whether laterality
differences across sex occur generally. Several objections
may be raised here. First, the fact that females tend to
exhibit a higher incidence of manual asymmetry than males
(e.g. Oldfield, 1971) is hard to reconcile with an
alleged stronger cerebral lateralization effect in males
(cf. Corballis, 1983). Second, it is quite plausible that
studies showing differences have received undue attention
at the expense of those showing organizational equivalence.
Third, some studies are likely to have confused intrahemispheric effects with interhemispheric ones (e.g.
Kimura, 1980; 1983).

In the field of bilingualism, our scepticism receives
further encouragement. When the sex factor was evaluated
statistically, we found that there was no reliable
difference between the sexes in the majority of cases.
Although sex data are not reported in many studies on
lateralization, nine investigations speaking explicitly
on the effects of this variable were encountered in the
specialist literature. Of these, six indicated organizational equivalence between males and females (e.g.
Galloway & Gottfried, 1982; Carroll, 1980; Hynd & Scott,
1980). It thus seems that in most cases no sex differences
in terms of language lateralization obtain, at least not
in the bilingual brain.

Age: The last of our individual-specific factors is
age. This variable is related to ontogenetic development,
and in particular to biological and cognitive maturation
of the brain (see e.g. Lenneberg, 1967). Investigations
of the possible effect of age on language lateralization
have however been hampered to a large extent by the
difficulty in isolating it from other intimately tied
parameters, especially verbal proficiency and intellectual
ability. Accordingly, it does not seem meaningful to

to discuss the hypothetical influence of age here, since
many of the pertinent studies are likely to have confounded
it with different age-related factors (cf. Clark & Knowles,
1973; Borod & Goodglass, 1979; Piazza & Zatorre, 1981).
The reader is instead referred to the discussion on L2-
proficiency below (p. 21), which probably houses the
factor of age as well in many instances.

3.2. Language-acquisitional factors

Age of acquiring L2: The age at which a person becomes
bilingual has attracted a great deal of interest. It has
been argued that if L2 is acquired subsequent to L1,
rather than simultaneously, one might expect differences
in neuropsychological organization for these languages,
since the maturational state of the brain differs during
the time of first versus second language acquisition
(Lamendella, 1977; Whitaker, 1978). Moreover, it has been
hypothesized that if the languages of a bilingual are
learnt successively, there will be a difference in
processing strategies between L1 and L2, since there are
differences in cognitive maturity (Hatch, 1977). These
ideas have led scholars to propose that the earlier L2-
acquisition takes place relative to L1-acquisition, the
more will the lateralization pattern of L2 conform to that
of L1. Stated more explicitly, late acquisition has been
associated with a lesser degree of hemispheric specialization, and it might therefore be expected that the
differences between simultaneous and successive L2-
acquisition manifests itself as a relatively greater
right-hemisphere involvement in late bilinguals as compared
to early bilinguals (e.g. Vaid & Genesee, 1980).

Turning to the research data, it appears that no
definite answer as to the effect of this factor on
lateralization in bilinguals is obtainable. In a comprehensive review, Galloway (1983) found 11 studies in favour of
differential lateralization patterns in early versus late
bilinguals - i.e. individuals having acquired L2 in infancy

or childhood versus such whose acquisition took place around puberty or later - where the former group showed equivalent left-hemisphere dominance for L1 and L2, and the latter less left-lateralization for L2 than L1 (e.g. Genesee et al., 1978; Sussman et al., 1980; Vaid & Lambert, 1979). On the other hand, there were 14 non-supportive studies, of which 12 implied roughly similar left-hemisphere patterns for L1 and L2 overall (e.g. Coulter, 1981; Gordon, 1980), and two opposed the hypothesis diametrically (Albert & Obler, 1978; Carroll, 1980). Thus, without conclusive evidence, the question as to whether age of acquiring L2 is a factor in the establishment of hemispheric specialization, and in particular whether the neuropsychological processes underlying verbal performance in those individuals who learn L2 late relative to L1 show more bilaterality than the "standard" pattern evinced by early bilinguals, has to be left in abeyance until more research is carried out on the topic.

Manner of acquiring L2: Explanations of different lateralization patterns have also been sought in the manner in which people acquire L2. One hypothesis states that the distinction between formal and informal modes of language acquisition is of particular relevance to brain organization in bilinguals. Formal acquisition refers to an artificial learning situation, often implicating a great deal of reading and writing, while informal acquisition denotes a naturalistic, communicational method, based on aural and oral skills. The line of reasoning rests on the fact that children (less than five years), who typically acquire language informally, are more liable to become aphasic following right-hemisphere lesions than adults (30% versus 10% according to Zangwill, 1967), who in contrast often show a formal, metalinguistic approach to language. This may be interpreted as showing that the right hemisphere is more involved in informal than formal language acquisition. Moreover, around the age of five, children tend to evince a shift from a relatively bilateral hemispheric involvement in language towards greater left-hemisphere dominance, corresponding to an increasingly

formal mode of language processing with cognitive
maturation (Witelson, 1977; Rosansky, 1975). Thus, as
cognitive functioning becomes more abstract and analytic,
approaching that of adults, a concomitant lateralization
of language processing in favour of the left hemisphere
appears to take place. The corollary of this argument
would be to associate formal L2-learning with an extent
of left-hemisphere participation greater than that of L1,
since as a rule it involves a substantially higher degree
of metalinguistic learning, and to couple the quality of
informal L2-acquisition with that of L1, resulting in an
approximate equivalence of left-hemisphere dominance for
these languages (Carroll, 1980).

On the whole, the above prediction is corroborated by
the research data. Galloway (1983) reported that out of
13 available studies on the topic, 11 seemed to espouse,
wholly or partially, the hypothesis that there is greater
left-hemisphere participation in the processing of L2 than
in L1 if L2 is acquired formally, and that there is no
appreciable difference of lateralization between L1 and
L2 if L2 is acquired informally (e.g. Kotik, 1975;
Coulter, 1981; Rogers et al., 1977). The two studies which
did not support the prediction exhibited an opposite
relationship, with formal L2-acquisition yielding less
left-hemisphere specialization than L1 (Maitre, 1974;
Schneiderman & Wesche, 1983). Hence, we may say that
manner of acquiring L2 seems to be a factor in the
progressive development of lateralization patterns in
bilinguals, and that the left hemisphere, contrary to
previous suggestions (e.g. Vildomec, 1963; Ovcharova et
al., 1968), apparently is particularly well predisposed to
formal L2-acquisition.

Proficiency in L2: Another factor which has received a
great deal of attention in this context is the degree of
proficiency in L2. Discussions of the possible influence
of this variable have centered around the stage hypothesis,
originally proposed by Obler et al. (1975), in which it
was suggested that the right hemisphere is relatively more
involved in the initial, non-proficient stages of L2-

acquisition than in the final, advanced stages. The
initially enhanced extent of right-hemisphere processing
was seen as a consequence of certain verbal strategies on
the part of the learner, which appear compatible with the
repertoire of right-hemisphere linguistic capabilities.
These strategies include, for example, reliance on prosodic
rather than phonetic features, content rather than function
words, and pragmatic rather than syntactic information
(McLaughlin, 1978), components of language which typically
have been associated with the abilities of the right
hemisphere (e.g. Blumstein & Cooper, 1974; Searleman,
1977). Furthermore, the hypothesis implies that as the
learner grows more proficient in L2, he will gradually
assume the set of verbal strategies used in L1, which then
would entail that the lateralization pattern of L2
eventually will conform to that of L1, thus resulting in
stable left-hemisphere dominance for both languages.

Contradicting expectations, the stage hypothesis has
generally been refuted by the empirical data. In a critical
review, Genesee (1982) found only five studies in favour
of the notion of greater right-hemisphere processing of
L2 during the initial stages of acquisition, of which only
three lent unconditional support (Bever, 1974; Kotik, 1975;
Silverberg et al., 1979). On the other hand, there were
10 non-supportive studies, of which six indicated
comparable lateralization patterns between L1 and L2
(e.g. Hardyck et al., 1978; Kershner & Jeng, 1972) and
four showed diametrically opposed results to the hypothesis,
with relatively greater right-hemisphere processing of L2
in proficient bilinguals (e.g. Genesee et al., 1978;
Vaid & Lambert, 1979).

The failure of the stage hypothesis led Krashen &
Galloway (1978) to propose an amended version of this
theory, the modified stage hypothesis. They suspected that
the preceding apparently conflicting findings were due to
an interaction between proficiency in L2 and manner of
acquiring L2, where the distinction between formal and
informal modes of L2-acquisition was of crucial importance.
The amended hypothesis thus predicted that the enhanced
extent of initial right-hemisphere processing would be

present only in those individuals who acquired their L2
informally, whereas the formal learners would exhibit a
stable pattern of left-hemisphere dominance irrespective
of proficiency level. However, neither of the two investigations undertaken to evaluate this model succeeded
in corroborating it (Galloway & Scarcella, 1982; Galloway,
1980).

Thus, it remains largely uncertain whether the factor
of proficiency in L2 has any effect on bilingual
lateralization patterns. The hypothesized extended
involvement of the right hemisphere in the early stages
of L2-acquisition, whether generalized or referring to
informal acquirers only, remains a matter of speculation
as most of the evidence did not support it.

3.3. Language-specific factors

Cognitive mode: Certain language-specific features
have also been proposed as potential determiners of
lateralization patterns. One such is cognitive mode, in
which language is seen as processed in either an appositional or a propositional manner. This distinction was
envisaged by Bogen (1969), who claimed that the right
hemisphere typically uses an appositional mode of thought
(involvement with the perceptual field), while the left
hemisphere is characterized by a propositional cognitive
manner (abstraction from the perceptual field; cf. p. 14).
In discussions of language-specific properties, it has
been argued that languages like Hopi and Navajo tend to
elicit appositional processing, whereas others, for
example English, tend to favour propositional processing
(e.g. Kaplan & TenHouten, 1975; Critchley, 1974). Hence,
if the linguistic competence of a bilingual involves one
appositional and one propositional language, one might
expect a difference in lateralization between these,
where the former would display a relatively higher
degree of right-hemisphere participation than the latter
(cf. Vaid & Genesee, 1980).

We have found three studies in the literature which consider this issue. In a test of Hopi-English bilinguals, Rogers et al. (1977) discovered a relatively greater involvement of the right hemisphere in Hopi as compared to English, though both languages still relied primarily on the left hemisphere. Scott et al. (1979) and Hynd & Scott (1980), on the other hand, reported a right-hemisphere advantage for language processing in Navajo-English bilinguals, while their monolingual English controls evinced a left-hemisphere advantage. Although these findings may be viewed as support for the hypothesis of a language-specific lateralization effect related to the alleged appositional mode of processing in Hopi and Navajo, caution is recommended, since there are a number of flaws in the experimental designs of these tests, which make alternative explanations equally possible (Rogers et al., 1977; Vaid & Genesee, 1980). For the time being, it will suffice to be aware of the probable existence of the distinction of appositional versus propositional mode of language processing in the brain, without drawing further conclusions until more research is carried out on the phenomenon.

Script: Two variables pertaining to the writing system have been associated with differential lateralization in bilinguals. The first involves a learning-to-read effect, which is thought to arise when a L2-acquirer is faced with a foreign type of script in relation to his vernacular, e.g. Chinese or Hebrew versus English. The hypothesis as to the influence of this factor is founded on the assumption that the right hemisphere is superior at processing novel visual shapes (e.g. Gordon & Carmon, 1976), and therefore better equipped to handle the initial acquisition of a new type of script, whether phonetic or ideographic. From this, it has been suggested that L2-acquirers learning to read a foreign script might show a relatively greater right-hemisphere involvement of L2-processing in the early stages, an effect which would disappear as they grow more familiar with the script of L2 (cf. Galloway, 1983).

On the whole, the relevant research data seem to endorse this hypothesis. Of the nine studies we found on the subject, seven favoured the idea of an initial right-hemisphere component in learning to read a novel L2-script (e.g. Silverberg et al., 1979; Bentin, 1981; Vaid, 1981), and two went against (Shimizu & Endo, 1981; Endo et al., 1981a). The effect has been demonstrated in several different languages, including both phonetic – for example Hebrew and Hindi – and ideographic scripts – for example Chinese – and it therefore appears to be independent of type of script. Thus, the present evidence indicates that the learning-to-read factor is of relevance in conditioning lateralization patterns in bilinguals, and in particular that novel L2-writing systems tend to induce an enhanced extent of right-hemisphere processing in the early stages of acquisition.

The other variable, finally, refers to <u>type of script</u>.[5] It has been shown that ideographic scripts, and specifically single-character ideograms, as in Chinese and Kanji (Chinese characters used for Japanese loan words from Chinese), tend to evoke a relatively higher degree of right-hemisphere processing than phonetically-based alphabetical or syllabic writing systems, e.g. English or Kana (the Japanese syllabic script) respectively (e.g. Hardyck et al., 1977; Tsao et al., 1979; 1981). This difference has been explained in terms of a superior pattern recognition ability in the right hemisphere, which would be particularly well suited for decoding of structurally complex ideograms. The extended right-hemisphere participation seems to prevail as long as no left-hemisphere-based sequential analysis is required from multiple stimuli (e.g. Huang & Jones, 1980; Sasanuma et al., 1980). Applied to bilinguals knowing one script of each type, one might expect a more bilateral processing distribution of the ideographic script, caused by the

---

5. Reading scan effects are not treated here, since they are considered as perceptual only, with no known neuropsychological implications in the context of lateralization.

enhanced right-hemisphere activity for this kind of
stimuli, as compared to the phonetic writing system,
which would exhibit the usual, clear pattern of left-
hemisphere dominance (cf. Galloway, 1983).

Broadly speaking, the prediction seems to be borne
out by the pertinent investigations. If the discussion is
confined to single-character ideograms versus phonetic
writing in general, some 20 studies lend support to the
hypothesis that the ideographic scripts evoke a greater
extent of right-hemisphere involvement than phonetic
scripts (e.g. Hatta, 1978; Endo et al., 1981b; Watamori &
Sasanuma, 1978). On the other hand, if sequences of
ideograms are taken into account, the picture becomes
less clear because of conflicting lateralization evidence
for the ideographic scripts (e.g. Kershner & Jeng, 1972;
Sasanuma, 1974). This latter unresolved state is probably
due to the effect of a left-hemisphere sequential analysis
carried out on the different combinations of ideograms,
which thus may obscure possible right-hemisphere processing to a greater or lesser extent.

Nevertheless, there is considerable evidence for
partially distinct neuropsychological processing of
ideographic and phonetic scripts in the brain, where
the right hemisphere apparently is particularly prone
to decoding of single-character ideograms. It should be
noted, however, that potential left- and right-hemisphere
processing of a certain script does not necessarily
entail that the language in general is also processed
mainly by that hemisphere, since in many individuals
spelling constitutes only a secondary representation
of a primary auditory-oral language system.

Summing up this section, then, we have briefly reviewed
clinical and experimental data on 10 circumstantial factors,
which have been proposed as conditioners of language
lateralization in bilinguals. Of these, only hand preference
seems to bear a clear relation to hemispheric organization.
Among the nine residual factors, considerable evidence
has been adduced for the relevance of familial handedness,
manner of acquiring L2, learning to read a foreign script,

and type of script, while it remains largely unresolved
whether sex, age, age of acquiring L2, proficiency in L2,
and cognitive mode influence bilingual lateralization in
any measurable way.

4. Auditory dichotic test

With the previous discussion of potential lateralization
factors in mind, we will now turn to the presentation of
our first experiment on bilingual lateralization – the
auditory dichotic test. Before going into the more
specific aims and hypotheses of this experiment, however,
it seems appropriate to briefly describe the test technique
and the anatomical and neuropsychological properties on
which it is founded.

The dichotic listening method was introduced in its
present form in the early 1960s by Kimura (1961a), who was
one of the pioneers within psychometric language research
on the human brain. She used a test paradigm, previously
devised by Broadbent (1954), in which different series of
short words were presented simultaneously to each ear, and
subjects were required to report as many of the heard
items as possible. In general, it was found that more
words were identified from the right ear than from the
left, an effect which obtained only with competitive,
dichotic stimulation, but not with successive, monaural
presentation (i.e. when the words were channelled to one
ear at a time). Since the basic capability of detecting
sounds does not differ between the ears, Kimura concluded
that the observed ear asymmetry had a neurophysiological
explanation related to the concept of cerebral dominance.
She capitalized on the neuroanatomy being crossed in
humans in such a way that each cerebral hemisphere
receives information primarily from the opposite half
of the body. Although the auditory system is somewhat
less crossed than other sensory systems, each half of the
brain being connected with both ears, the crossed neural
pathways nevertheless seem to be prepotent (cf. Bocca et al.,

1955). To account for the right-ear superiority, Kimura
postulated that the ipsilateral pathways were occluded or
inhibited during dichotic presentation of verbal material.
In order to reach the language-dominant left hemisphere,
input from the left ear thus would have to cross over to
the right hemisphere via the contralateral pathway, and
then be routed back to the left through the corpus
callosum (the major bundle of neural fibers connecting
the hemispheres), while input from the right ear would
project directly to the left hemisphere via the contralateral pathway (see Figure 1). Presumably, this difference
of direct and indirect access to the left hemisphere is
responsible for the typical differential accuracy of
word identification in favour of the right ear (but see
Mononen & Seitz, 1977; Studdert-Kennedy, 1975).

   Seen from another perspective, ear asymmetry patterns
may be used as measures of the direction and extent of
hemispheric specialization of language. Kimura (1961b)
noted that clinical findings on cerebral dominance from
both aphasiological investigations and sodium amytal
tests (e.g. Wada & Rasmussen, 1960; Rasmussen & Milner,
1977) correlated quite well with ear scores obtained in
dichotic listening. On the basis of this, she claimed that
ear advantages demonstrated with the dichotic method are
reliable indicators of contralateral hemispheric
dominance, and that the extent of lateralization is
proportional to the magnitude of the recorded ear
difference.

   In essence, Kimura's line of reasoning has subsequently
been confirmed by the joint results of clinical and
experimental studies (e.g. Branch et al., 1964; Curry,
1967; Hines & Satz, 1974). Though the dichotic listening
test is necessarily confined to language reception,
specifically to relatively short verbal stimuli, it
has yielded an interesting and informative picture of
how the brain presumably processes these aspects of
language, and thereby supplemented and differentiated
several neurolinguistic findings and theories from the
clinical domain.

Figure 1

Human head seen from behind. The auditory pathways
extending from the ears to the cerebral auditory receiving
areas (Herschl's gyri) are indicated. The cochlear nuclei
are the regions where the main neural fibers from each
ear are split up into an ipsilateral (broken line) and
a contralateral pathway (continuous line). (Adapted from
Kimura's (1973) simplified model.)

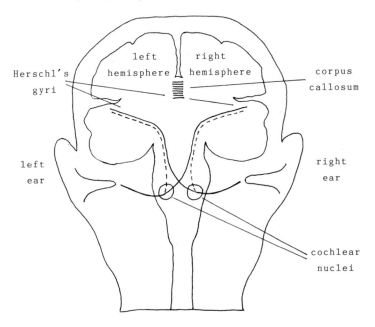

Our own experiment will investigate the interhemispheric
distribution of lexical processing in the brains of
Swedish-English subsidiary bilinguals. The aim is to
throw some light on the relative lateralization of Swedish
and English receptive word-processing and to relate
possible differences to certain factors. In particular, we
want to examine the potential influence of some of the
factors discussed in Section 3, viz. manner of acquiring
L2, proficiency in L2, age, sex, and familial handedness
as measured by a bilingual dichotic listening task.

To accomplish this, an appropriate test paradigm was
designed, with parallel tests of Swedish and English words,
which were chosen to represent a cross-section of the
basic vocabulary in each of the languages. The words were
carefully matched in several respects in order to form
comparable stimulus conditions, and to minimize the
effects of inadequate language-specific factors. Further,
a proper test population was selected, where each of the
target variables was controlled or manipulated to create
an apt basis for expedient and adequate hypothesis testing.
The participating subjects were all dextral[6] Swedes who
had learnt English at school as a foreign language (formal
acquirers); they were divided into three different groups
on the basis of proficiency level in English, a division
which interacted with the factor of age, as a result of
which these two factors had to be treated as a compound
denoted age/English proficiency level. Moreover, in each
age/proficiency group, there was an equal number of males
and females, and a certain proportion of subjects who
reported having familial left-handers (for a more thorough
description of the test population and the stimuli, see
Section 4.2).

   Below, we will try to formulate a number of hypotheses
pertaining to the effects or lack of effects of the above
factors on language lateralization in our type of
bilinguals, based on the previous review of research
within the field. These predictions will constitute our
working hypotheses in the experiment and serve as targets
for the postexperimental statistical analyses.

----

6. Left-handers and ambidextrals will be largely ignored
throughout this thesis. By this we do not mean to say
that these individuals are less interesting than right-
handers regarding language organization (on the contrary,
rather), but their exclusion is merely a result of our
trying to keep the test population as homogeneous yet broad
as possible. Naturally, we are primarily interested in the
neuropsychological status of average bilinguals, and non-
dextrality obtains in around 10% of individuals only (e.g.
Rife, 1951; Oldfield, 1971; cf. Coren & Porac, 1977).

4.1. Hypotheses

A majority of studies on bilingual lateralization have
indicated that as a rule both languages are processed
primarily by the left hemisphere (see p. 1; cf. Sections 1
and 2). This is especially true in right-handers and if
the languages involved do not differ with regard to the
language-specific factors previously discussed, i.e.
cognitive mode and properties of the writing system (see
p. 23 ff.). Since our test population consists of dextrals
only, and Swedish and English have similar values on each
of the language-specific variables, we expect that both
languages will show left-hemisphere dominance. Thus,
Hypothesis I predicts that both the Swedish and the
English stimuli will be processed primarily by the left
hemisphere.

As we have seen, however, there are a number of
occasions on which different degrees of left-hemisphere
specialization have obtained for L1 and L2. One of the
most influential conditioners of differential lateralization patterns seems to be manner of language acquisition
(which incidentally covary with age of L2-acquisition in
our subjects) - 11 out of 13 studies supported the notion
that formal acquisition entails a greater extent of left-
hemisphere involvement than informal acquisition (see p.
20 f.). As L1 (Swedish), being a native language, was
acquired informally by our subjects and L2 (English)
primarily formally, it appears plausible to assume that
L2 will be more left-lateralized than L1 in the experiment.
Hypothesis II accordingly forecasts that the English
stimuli will engender a higher degree of left-hemisphere
processing than the Swedish stimuli.

Moreover, it has also been argued that different levels
of proficiency in L2 will contribute to differential
lateralization in bilinguals. However, since the majority
of relevant studies supported neither the original stage
hypothesis (10 versus 5) nor its modified version (2 versus
0), i.e. that there is less left-hemisphere dominance for
L2 in the initial stages of acquisition (see p. 21 ff.),
this theory must be rejected at present. Instead, as most

of the studies (6) indicated comparable degrees of left-lateralization for L2 irrespective of proficiency level, and thus probably age as well, we assume that the age/English proficiency factor is irrelevant to hemispheric specialization of language in our three groups of bilinguals. Hence, Hypothesis III predicts that there will be no difference of lateralization attributable to the factor of age/proficiency in English.

Further, no reliable effect of subject sex has been recorded in this context. Although there is occasionally a tendency for females to display lower laterality than males, the predominant pattern seems to be equal cerebral asymmetry across sex (see p. 17 f.). Consequently, this is what one would expect also from the present experiment. Hypothesis IV thus states that males and females will show equivalent patterns of left-hemisphere lateralization.

Finally, some studies have indicated that the factor of familial handedness influences language lateralization. Those individuals who report having familial sinistrals tend to exhibit a generally less pronounced pattern of left-hemisphere dominance than similar subjects without such family members (see p. 17). If this is true, a comparable effect would obtain in the relevant part of our subject sample. Hence, Hypothesis V predicts that subjects with familial left-handers will show less left-hemisphere lateralization than subjects with a negative value on this variable.

4.2. Description

Subjects: The subjects were selected for the experiment in accordance with the following specifications. (1) Subsidiary bilingualism.[7] The subjects should have Swedish as their

---

7. Most of the subjects were in fact subsidiary multilinguals, as they had done some German and/or French as well as English. Since our focus is on one foreign language only, however, we will adhere to the term subsidiary bilinguals.

native language and English as their first foreign
language. (2) <u>Educational and proficiency level</u>. Each
subject should belong to one of the following educational
groups: Group A = ninth-graders at the comprehensive
school, Group B = first-term students of English at
university, and Group C = third-term students of English
at university. Further, in order to make a higher
educational level coincide as much as possible with a
higher proficiency level in English, the subjects in
Group A were required to have achieved either level three
or level four in English (on a five-point scale with five
as the highest mark, the assessment being made during
the preceding term). Group B subjects were required to
have achieved scores between nine and 13 on a vocabulary
test[8] (range = 1-20 points) standardized within the
English Department at the University of Göteborg. Group C
subjects were required to have achieved scores between 16
and 20 points on the same test. (3) <u>Age of acquiring L2</u>.
Since most Swedes commence their studies of English at
around the age of 10, we set this value as a general
starting-age prerequisite so as to keep the language
backgrounds as similar as possible. (4) <u>Dextrality</u>. All
participants were required to be right-handers. To check
this, they did a writing test and, on the lines of
Oldfield's (1971) hand preference inventory, they gave
a handedness self-report about several aspects of hand
preference, e.g. brushing of teeth, holding a receiver,
and throwing a ball. (5) <u>Normal hearing</u>. Subjects' left
and right ear were required to be equally good and in
general not crucially impaired. The simplest standard
medical test - i.e. monaural identification of whispered
digits - was used to ascertain that all the testees
conformed to this requirement. (Due to various practical
problems, no audiometry was performed.)

    In addition to the above five constraints on the
individual subjects, there were also two group qualifications and one general recruitment restriction: (6) <u>Number</u>

---

8. This test is given routinely to all our university
students of English.

of subjects. Each group should contain 20 subjects.
(7) Sex distribution. There should be 10 males and 10
females in each group. (8) Recruitment area. For practical
reasons, the geographical area of subject recruitment was
restricted to Göteborg. Group A subjects were drawn from
a single school, the Burås Comprehensive School; Group B
and Group C subjects came from the English Department at
the University of Göteborg. Altogether, then, the test
population came to consist of 60 subjects, distributed
into three equally large groups, with an equal number of
males and females.

 The lowest proficiency group, Group A, had studied
English two to three 40-minute periods per week for about
five years, and had a mean age of 15:8 years[9] (range =
15:1-16:2 years). The intermediate group, Group B, had a
school history of two to three 40-minute periods of
English per week for approximately nine years, and had a
mean age of 22:7 years (range = 18:10-26:5 years). The
highest proficiency group, Group C, had a similar pre-
university school background to that of Group B, plus an
additional full time year as students of English at
university, and had a mean age of 23:5 years (range =
20:6-27:9 years).

 Moreover, since the value of the age factor covaried
with the value of the proficiency factor, these variables
had to be treated as a compound factor referred to as
age/English proficiency level. Though not mentioned before,
it was suspected that this factor had a third component
as well, viz. intellectual capability. It seems reasonable
to assume that the higher the educational/proficiency
level is, the higher is the average intellectual capacity
level, because there is a progressive selection in favour
of students with a high intellectual ability as the
requirements of scholastic achievement increase. In other
words, this would be an effect of the so-called drop-out
factor.

 In order to test this idea, an investigation of subjects'

---

9. Age is given in years and months - 15:8 years, for
example, means 15 years and eight months.

final marks in Swedish and mathematics from the gymnasium[10]
(Groups B and C) and the eighth grade of the comprehensive
school (Group A) was carried out, marks which summarized
and averaged may be viewed as a rough measure of intellectual
ability in the respective groups (cf. Nordlund, 1975;
Vernon, 1960). However, as the marks gauge the ability of
each subject category exclusively in relation to its own
educational peers, and the peers of Group A were qualita-
tively different from those of Group B and Group C, an
unbiased overall comparison was precluded. Presumably,
the mean score of Group A (3.85) was inflated as compared
to the other two groups, since there tends to be less
severe competition for high marks in the obligatory
comprehensive school than in the optional gymnasium due
to a lack of natural student selection at this level.
This condition compelled us to set the data from Group A
aside here.

Between Group B and Group C, which are theoretically
directly comparable regarding educational peers and
therefore also regarding mark competition, a considerable
difference was found in favour of Group C (3.92 versus 3.70).
These results tally quite well with our notion that there
is an increase of intellectual ability with educational/
proficiency level, provided that there is a positive
correlation between the values of school marks and
intellectual status. Thus, although no immediate support
was obtainable from the mean score of Group A, it appears
necessary to view the factor of intellectual ability as
conditioned by the student drop-out factor and therefore
nested within the age/English proficiency factor in our
test population.

Each subject was also questioned about possible
familial sinistrality, the value of this factor being
defined as affirmative if any parent or sibling was left-
handed. Five such instances were found in Group A, three
in Group B, and four in Group C.

Finally, all subjects were experimentally naive in the

---

10. The Swedish gymnasium is roughly equivalent to the sixth
form in Great Britain or the senior high school in the US.

sense that they had never participated in experiments of
the present type. They volunteered for the tests when
asked and received a small sum of money in return for
their participation.

Stimuli: 60 Swedish and 60 English words were used as
stimuli in the experiment. Each language sample was
selected to be of a corresponding level of difficulty
in the sense that the words in one language matched those
in the other in terms of word-length, range of frequency,
and word category. The words were thus either three or
four letters long, and ranged from high to moderate
frequency (Allén, 1970; Kučera & Francis, 1967). They
were equally distributed over the three main word-classes,
yielding 20 nouns, 20 verbs, and 20 adjectives in each
language. This interlanguage correspondence of stimuli
was maintained in order to create as broad and parallel
test batteries as possible, suitable for equivalent
probings of the organization of the underlying lexical
correlates.

Further, within each word-class group, the words were
paired, each member of a pair to be phonetically and
structurally similar to the other on the basis of the
following three criteria: (1) Each member of the pairs
should have the same number of phonemes in front of the
stress phoneme. (2) The initial phoneme of each member
should belong to the same group of phonemes, i.e. be
either a vowel, plosive, fricative, nasal, or liquid.
(3) Each member should contain the same number of
phonemes.[11] These restrictions were introduced in order
to increase the difficulty of the discriminability
process and thereby evoke a more adequate magnitude of
the potential differences between the ears.

The resulting 30 word-pairs in each language (10 nominal,

---

11. Vowels of long duration, as in need /ni:d/ and true
/tru:/, were counted as if containing two phonemes, and
were thus considered as equivalent to diphthongs in, for
example, make /meik/ and ride /raid/ concerning number
of phonemes.

10 verbal, and 10 adjectival pairs) were thereafter used
to produce an inverted version of each pair, e.g. forming
step - skin from skin - step and äga - öka from öka - äga,
making a total of 60 pairs in each language. These word-
pairs were randomized[12] separately for the Swedish and
the English part and divided into blocks of three pairs
(cf. the design of Kimura, 1961a). The blocks were in
their turn combined into instalments of four blocks,
yielding five different instalments out of 20 blocks in
each language (see Appendix).

When the arrangement of the stimuli was finished, all
the word-pairs were recorded dichotically on a micro-
processed multi-track tape recorder (Otari MTR 90).
One language at a time was attended to, and both the
Swedish and the English words were read by the experimenter.
The left members of the pairs were recorded on one channel
and the right members on another, and to achieve a rough
synchronization and periodicity of the stimuli during
these sessions, a metronome was used, recorded on a third
channel. The beats of the metronome were relayed to the
experimenter via a headset and thus served as a pacing
guide during the reading of the words.

After the recording procedure, the two channels
containing the stimuli were transferred to a dual-channel
Audex 1/4" tape, and the words in each pair were matched
for temporal alignment, using an electronic auto-locater
connected to the tape recorder. This synchronization was
performed on the basis of simultaneous occurrences of the
respective stress phonemes of the words. Fluctuations of
intensity were also checked - first for each channel on
a mix-console during the recording session, and then for
the complete dichotic tape on an oscilloscope with a
storage display unit. The intensity differences both
within and between pairs were found to be rather low and
never exceeded five dB.

From the master tape, five Swedish and five English

---

12. There was one restriction on this randomization,
however - the original and the inverted version of a word-
pair were not allowed within the same block.

copies with different pseudo-random orders of the respective
five instalments were produced. There were thus five
randomizations of the word-pairs available in each
language (see Appendix).

Apparatus: A Revox A-77 two-track tape recorder and a
pair of stereophonic earphones (model DH-207) were used in
the experiment. There were four procedural variables which
were counterbalanced across subjects. (1) Left-right
orientation of the earphones, (2) order of the Swedish
and the English test, (3) randomization of the word-pairs
in the Swedish test, and (4) randomization of the word-
pairs in the English test. The balancing of the first
variable was done to spread any channel effects equally
over the ears, whereas the distribution of the values of
the other three variables was carried out to reduce any
biases in the results due to warming-up effects or
practice effects.

Responses were written on prefabricated answer forms,
two for each language.

Procedure: All subjects were tested individually in
a quiet room. They were seated at a table, facing a
fixation-point on a white wall about 1.5 metres away,
and had the tape recorder out of sight behind them. The
experimenter gave the following instructions orally to
each subject in Swedish: "The present experiment is an
attempt to find out possible differences between the ways
in which Swedish and English words are treated in the
brain of native Swedish speakers. You will hear a number
of words in the earphones, and your task is to try to
remember as many of them as possible and subsequently to
write them down. The words will be given in pairs, i.e.
one word will be heard in the left ear at the same time
as another word is heard in the right ear, and they will
be presented in blocks, with three word-pairs in each
such block. A warning-signal precedes each trial, implying
that you should concentrate and fix your eyes on the
point on the wall right in front of you.[13] Don't write
anything during the presentation of a block - only try to

listen as closely as you can, attending to both ears. Try
also to avoid connecting the words you hear, for example
by making up small stories etc., since that may disturb
the processes we want to measure. When you have listened
to a block of words, you are to pick up your pen and write
down on the answer form as many of the six words presented
to you as you can recall. You may write them in any order
you like and you are free to guess when you are not sure.
There is no time limit on your responses - just put down
your pen when you have finished each block of words and
the tape recorder will be restarted for a new three-pair-
block presentation. You will be given one Swedish and one
English test and each of these contains 20 blocks."

Thereafter, the subjects were given a transcript[14] of
all the stimulus words involved in the experiment. Each
subject spent two to three minutes reading through the
body of words, and when he/she did not know the pronunciation or meaning of a word, this was explained to him/her.
In general, it was only the subjects in Group A, representing
the lowest English proficiency level, who exhibited some
minor problems with the vocabulary.

Subjects then received two practice blocks, one Swedish
and one English, which were not included in the test
material. The practice session was introduced to familiarize
the subjects with the testing procedure and to reduce
warming-up effects. After this, there was a short pause,
during which subjects were allowed to ask questions about
any possibly unclear aspects of the execution of the
experiment.

Before the test started, the predetermined randomization

---

13. It has been shown that lateral attention may influence
cerebral lateralization patterns in certain psycholinguistic
experiments (Kinsbourne, 1970). A fixation-point task was
therefore introduced in this test to prevent subjects from
swaying their focus to either side and thereby contaminating
the subsequent results of the experiment.

14. The transcript did not display the words in pairs,
but only as single items in the form of a random list.

of instalments for the subject being tested was located
on the dichotic tape. The experimenter operated the tape
recorder throughout the test and at the same time checked
from behind that subjects followed the instructions.
The arrival of each block was signalled by a warning-
tone recorded on both channels 3.0 seconds before the
first word-pair, and within a block the word-pairs were
presented at intervals of 2.0 seconds. All subjects
heard each word-pair twice - once in the original
orientation and once in the inverted version. This
balancing was meant to neutralize any bias in the
results caused by possible remaining differences of
intensity or temporal alignment within the word-pairs.
There was a short break between the Swedish and the
English test, and the whole experiment took approximately
30 minutes.

Scoring: The answer forms were manually corrected by
the experimenter. All words correctly recalled and
written were scored as one point. These also included
substitutions of phonological equivalents, for example
meat /mi:t/ or mete /mi:t/ and non-words such as miit
/mi:t/ representing the target phonological sequence,
but not non-corresponding misspellings, for example
mite /mait/ or mit /mit/, or illegible words, which
were scored as nil points.

4.3. Results

The postexperimental treatment of the test data
consisted of three different types of measure of lateral
advantage: (1) mean value computations of subjects' raw
scores, (2) summarized individual ear asymmetry patterns,
and (3) mean value computations of a specific laterality
index based on the raw scores. Statistics (analyses of
variance) were performed on two of these (1 and 3).
The mean raw scores from the auditory test are given
in Table 1. As can be seen, the grand mean of correct

responses equalled 34.2, or 57%, out of 60 possible in
each experimental condition. This value is within the
desired 50-80% interval, in which both substantial
laterality effects are allowed of and ceiling effects
are, if not ruled out completely, at least rather
unlikely (cf. Keppel, 1973).[15] The task must accordingly
be said to hold an appropriate level of difficulty.

   Among the incorrect responses, which thus amounted to
25.8, or 43%, in each test condition, the vast majority
consisted of blanks. The remainder was either unacceptable
misrepresentations of the stimuli or illegible words, the
occurrences of which were slightly more frequent in the
lower range of age/English proficiency than in the upper
(17% overall).

Table 1

Mean numbers of correctly reported words in each
experimental condition in the auditory test.

	Group A			Group B			Group C			
	M	F	Tot.	M	F	Tot.	M	F	Tot.	Total
Swe. RE	37.1	38.3	37.7	41.3	38.5	39.9	42.9	42.1	42.5	40.0
Swe. LE	28.4	33.5	30.9	37.1	32.2	34.6	37.7	38.8	38.2	34.6
Tot. Swe.	32.8	35.9	34.3	39.2	35.4	37.2	40.3	40.5	40.4	37.3
Eng. RE	28.7	27.8	28.2	37.2	31.4	34.3	39.2	33.2	36.2	32.9
Eng. LE	22.9	23.3	23.1	35.2	26.5	30.8	34.9	33.3	34.1	29.3
Tot. Eng.	25.8	25.6	25.7	36.2	29.0	32.5	37.1	33.3	35.1	31.1
Grand Tot.	29.3	30.8	30.0	37.7	32.2	34.9	38.7	36.9	37.7	34.2

RE = right ear, LE = left ear, M = males, F = females

---

15. Before the experiment, it was arbitrarily decided that
if any subject's hit-rate difference between the left and
right ears was greater than 50% of the total number of
identified words, his response data would be discarded
altogether. This rule was established in order to exclude
both subjects who contrary to test instructions applied
selective, monaural attention in carrying out the task - i.e.
attended essentially to one ear only (cf. Kinsbourne, 1970) -
and subjects with undetected, unilateral hearing deficits.
Fortunately, however, no such extreme response patterns obtained.

A four-way analysis of variance with repeated measures
involving age/English proficiency level (3) and sex (2)
as between-subject variables and language (2) and ear (2)
as within-subject variables was performed on the scores
in Table 1.[16] Three significant main effects emerged from
the analysis: <u>Age/English proficiency level</u>.[17] The total
mean number of correctly recalled stimulus words increased

---

16. In the analyses of variance throughout this thesis,
subjects were treated as a random factor and language
materials as a fixed factor. Clark (1973) has claimed
that both subjects and stimuli should be handled as
random factors in analyses of this type to avoid the
so-called "language-as-a-fixed-effect fallacy", i.e.
inappropriate generalization of experimental findings
from a limited stimulus sample to language in general.
His proposal requires, however, the use of certain
approximate or quasi F-ratios, which have not been
sufficiently explored mathematically to substantiate their
validity, nor have the power and robustness of this method
been demonstrated (Wike & Church, 1976). The application
of Clark's mode of analysis is therefore questionable.

Instead, the conventional statistical techniques and
properties were adhered to in the present analyses, with
only subjects as a random factor and accordingly non-
statistical generalizability primarily on the subject
sample. The generality power of the language materials
is, however, not completely lost by this method, but
generalizations may still be made, though requiring a
certain amount of circumspection.

17. It should be noted that the tripartite factor age/English
proficiency level has consistently been subject to omnibus
tests only - i.e. no pairwise comparisons (e.g. Newman-
Keul's test) have been computed to determine specifically
between which of the subject groups the possible significance occurred. We contented ourselves with this broad
statistical approach, since the primary aim of our
investigation was not to contrast the different groups
against each other, but rather to evaluate the general
influence of the age/proficiency factor.

with level of age/proficiency, i.e. Group A had the lowest
mean score (30.0), Group B was intermediate (34.9), and
Group C had the highest mean score (37.7), (F(2,54)=13.8,
p<.001).[18] Language. More Swedish than English words were
identified (mean numbers = 37.3 vs. 31.1), (F(1,54)=98.5,
p<.001). Ear. More words were correctly reported from the
right ear than from the left (mean numbers = 36.5 vs. 32.0),
(F(1,54)=32.3, p<.01).

No significant effect of sex emerged, but there was a
trend for males to be slightly superior to females on the
task (mean numbers = 35.2 vs. 33.2), (F(1,54)=2.6, p=.11).

There were also two significant two-way interactions:
Language x age/English proficiency level. The difference
between the mean scores of the Swedish and English tests
decreased from Group A (mean difference = 8.7) to Group B
(4.7) and Group C (5.2), (F(2,54)=3.9, p<.05). Language x
sex. Females exhibited a greater difference between the
scores in the Swedish and the English test than males
(mean differences = 8.0 vs. 4.4), (F(1,54)=8.2, p<.01).
No other interactions reached significance.

Since mean value computations obscure relevant data in
some instances, we will also give the experimental results
in terms of each individual subject's possible asymmetry
relation between the ears. This will be called REA when
the subject exhibits a right ear advantage, LEA for a

---

18. As will become apparent in the following, no statistics
on the response data in terms of standard deviation (SD)
or mean square error (MS_e) computations are given in the
results of any of our experiments. Although, at first, we
did not intend to report distribution measures of this
type, such figures were nevertheless routinely calculated
by the computer in each analysis of variance. When at
a late stage of the present work, Ulf Norrsell and Erland
Hjelmquist (personal communication) pointed out the
usefulness of these measures, we tried to recover the data,
but unfortunately it was lost (cleaned out probably). This
is why it is not included in the thesis. Our only consola-
tion is that SD- and MS_e-figures are left out in more
than one study in similar behavioural research.

left ear advantage, and RE=LE when the ears are equal. The
summarized scores from this laterality measure are presented
in Table 2.

Table 2

Numbers and percentages of subjects with a REA, LEA,
and RE=LE in the Swedish and the English part of the
auditory test.

	Group A		Group B		Group C		Total	
	number	%	number	%	number	%	number	%
Swe. REA	17	85	14	70	15	75	46	77
Swe. LEA	2	10	4	20	3	15	9	15
Swe. RE=LE	1	5	2	10	2	10	5	8
Eng. REA	14	70	11	55	12	60	37	62
Eng. LEA	4	20	6	30	8	40	18	30
Eng. RE=LE	2	10	3	15	0	0	5	8

No statistics were computed on the data in Table 2,
however, since these scores do not constitute the primary
measure through which the experimental hypotheses will be
evaluated. This was saved for our third and most important
type of measure - the laterality index.

Previous lateralization studies have shown that the
laterality effect in certain circumstances is a function
of task difficulty (e.g. Satz et al., 1965; Satz, 1968)
and thus overall performance, and since the levels of
overall performance in the present experiment varied
substantially, both within and between the Swedish and
the English test, it was considered necessary to compute
a specific laterality index (LI) to achieve a measure of
lateralization unbiased for overall performance
fluctuations (Marshall et al., 1975).[19] The chosen index

---

19. A post hoc correlation test was calculated on the
laterality indices and their corresponding total raw
scores (R+L) to determine whether or not the index measure
covaried with overall performance in the experiment. It
was found that the Swedish LIs correlated significantly
with the total Swedish scores ($r = -.36$, $p<.01$), while
the English LIs did not reach a significant correlation

was produced by transformation of each subject's raw
score in each experimental condition (see Table 1)
using the formula LI = ((R-L)/(R+L))x100, i.e. the
difference between the scores of the right and left ear
divided by the total number of correct responses and
multiplied by 100. A positive value of the index (LI>0)
would then indicate a right ear advantage and a negative
value (LI<0) a left ear advantage, while LI=0 would
mean that no difference exists between the ears. In
Table 3, the mean values of the laterality index are
given.

Table 3

Mean values of the laterality index in the different
experimental conditions in the auditory test.

	Group A			Group B			Group C			Total
	M	F	Tot.	M	F	Tot.	M	F	Tot.	
Swe. LI	14.5	6.2	10.4	5.1	9.8	7.5	7.2	3.9	5.6	7.8
Eng. LI	12.1	8.6	10.4	2.5	9.2	5.9	6.4	-.01	3.2	6.5
Total LI	13.3	7.4	10.4	3.8	9.5	6.7	6.8	2.0	4.4	·7.1

Apparently, all experimental conditions except one in
the table above yielded a right ear advantage. Only Group C
females in the English test broke rank with a negative mean
index of laterality (a left ear advantage), and this was
then of a very marginal magnitude (LI=-.01). If the
laterality indices are plotted as a function of age/Eng-
lish proficiency level for males and females in the
Swedish and the English test respectively, Figures 2 and
3 emerge.

As we can see, there is a marked variation of the sex
factor in each of the three subject groups in both
languages. Both figures contain strongly disordinal

with the English totals (r = -.24, p=.07). (The negative
value of the correlation coefficient is to be interpreted
as a decrease of the LI-value when the total score
increases.) The Swedish lateralization patterns may thus
be considered as more related to level of overall performance than the English patterns (but cf. note 34).

LATERALIZATION

Figure 2

Laterality for males and females as a function of age/English proficiency level in the Swedish part of the auditory test.

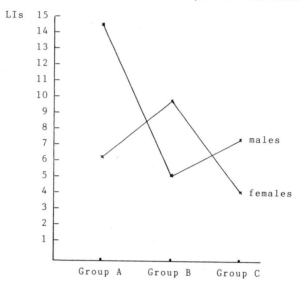

Figure 3

Laterality for males and females as a function of age/English proficiency level in the English part of the auditory test.

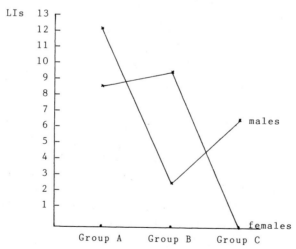

curves and the patterns seem on the whole rather hard to
interpret unequivocally. If we collapse the LIs across
sex and render the data graphically again, however, a
different and quite neat pattern emerges.

<u>Figure 4</u>

Laterality as a function of age/English proficiency level
in the Swedish and English parts of the auditory test.

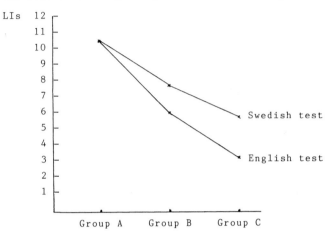

After all, then, there appear to exist fairly clear and
regular trends in the LI-data from this experiment.
English words tend to engender lower LIs than Swedish words
(6.5 vs. 7.8), there is a propensity for the LIs to
decrease with increasing age/English proficiency level
(Group A = 10.4, Group B = 6.7, and Group C = 4.4), and
females show a tendency towards lower LIs than males
(6.3 vs. 8.0). The LI-difference between Swedish and
English is greatest for Group C (2.4), followed by Group B
(1.6), while it is non-existent for Group A.

In order to test whether any of the perceived LI-
differences are reliable, a three-way analysis of variance
with repeated measures (age/English proficiency level (3),
sex (2), and language (2)) was carried out. Contrary to
expectations, this statistical treatment revealed that
there were neither any significant main effects nor any
significant interactions in the data. Closest to reach

significance were the factor age/English proficiency level
(F(2,54)=1.8, p=.18) and an age/English proficiency level x
sex interaction (F(2,54)=2.0, p=.15).

   To assess whether an ear effect in one language was
related to an ear effect in the other language, a correlation test was conducted on the Swedish and English
laterality indices. The result was a significant r = .53
(p<.001), indicating that the extents of ear asymmetry
for L1 and L2 were interrelated to a rather high degree
in the individual subjects.

   Finally, concerning the influence of familial handedness on the present data, a separate three-way analysis
of variance with repeated measures (familial handedness[20]
(2), language (2), and ear (2)) was computed on the LIs.
Despite a seemingly marked difference (subjects with
familial sinistrals = 11.9 vs. such without = 2.4), no
significant main effect emerged (F(1,58)=.1, p=.73), nor
were there any significant interactions.

4.4. Discussion

   The results of the present experiment demonstrate that
dextral Swedish-English subsidiary bilinguals as a rule
show a significant right ear advantage for the processing
of both Swedish and English auditory lexical stimuli (ear -
raw scores; cf. Tables 1, 2, and 3). According to previous
reasoning (see p. 28), this finding suggests that both
languages are processed somewhat more by the left hemisphere and that the bilingual lexical system therefore
depends more on the neuropsychological mechanisms of this
hemisphere than those of the right. Such a conclusion is
consistent with the vast majority of previous studies on
bilingual lateralization, which have indicated that the
left hemisphere is usually dominant for verbal processing

---

20. The familial sinistrality scores were pooled over
age/English proficiency level in the present experiment,
as well as in the following visual one.

irrespective of language. Thus, the prediction of
Hypothesis I that both languages would show a left-
hemisphere advantage is confirmed.

Regarding the extent of left-lateralization, there
seems to be no reliable difference between the Swedish
and English lexical representations. Although there was
a clear tendency for the Swedish words to induce a
higher degree of left-hemisphere processing than the
English words (see Figure 4), this difference did not
reach significance, presumably because the heterogeneity
was too high in the intralanguage data. At any rate,
Hypothesis II, i.e. that L2 would display more left-
lateralization than L1, is not supported by the present
results, since it proposed a difference in a direction
opposite to that of the trend obtained. Rather, despite
the distinction of manner of acquisition, auditorily-
presented Swedish and English words seem to induce roughly
similar hemispheric patterns of neuropsychological processing. This conclusion is also corroborated by there
being a significant correlation between the Swedish
and English LIs, a finding which implies that in the
individual subjects a strong lateralization in L1 is
usually accompanied by a similar pattern in L2, or
conversely, that a weak or non-existent lateralization
in L1 is coupled with a similar state in L2.

The age/English proficiency factor gave a similar
picture to that of the language factor. There was a clear
tendency in both languages for the extent of left-hemisphere
dominance to decrease with increasing age/proficiency
level (see Figure 4), but the effect did not reach
statistical significance, probably due to a high variation
also in the intragroup LI-data. Contrary to the preceding
factor, however, this roughly stable pattern is in
accordance with the preexperimental prediction - Hypothesis
III - i.e. that there would be no difference of laterality
attributable to the factor of age/English proficiency
level. Accordingly, the interhemispheric distribution
of the bilingual lexical mechanisms has to be viewed as
remaining more or less stable over the interval of
age/proficiency examined, at least as measured through the

auditory modality.

   Finally, regarding our hypotheses of sex and familial
handedness, neither of these factors seems to have
induced any appreciable differences of lateralization.
In the former case, the predicted approximate equivalence
between males and females obtained, which thus confirms
the notion of Hypothesis IV that the sex factor would not
exercise any significant influence on hemispheric
processing patterns in our subjects. In the latter case,
the effect of familial handedness fell short of expectations. The hypothesized lower laterality in subjects with
left-handed parents or siblings was not found; on the
contrary, there was a tendency in the opposite direction,
with this category showing higher laterality than
"ordinary" subjects. The difference did not reach
significance, however, and for now, it will suffice to
recognize that the prediction of Hypothesis V was not
validated by the auditory experiment. (See further
Section 6.2 for an explanative discussion of the overall
results of the lateralization experiments.)

5. Visual monotic test

   Having probed the organization of the bilingual lexical
system through the auditory modality, we will now proceed
to the visual domain. Our second experiment on cerebral
lateralization - the visual monotic test[21] - has been
devised in order to create a visual analogue to the
preceding dichotic listening test. The experimental
paradigm consists of a modified, computerized version of
the conventional tachistoscopic viewing procedure, which

---

21. The neologistic term _monotic_ is introduced here
merely as a contrast to _dichotic_ (cf. "monotomy" vs.
dichotomy). It is applied to differentiate the two
stimulus-presentation techniques of our lateralization
tests, with the monotic method denoting single-item
exposure and the dichotic dual-item exposure.

has been in frequent use in various forms of psycholinguistic research during the past few decades.
Hopefully, the results of this parallel method will
complement the previous auditory findings and contribute
to a more crystallized picture of the verbal organization
of the brain in our target population. First, however,
before any further presentation of the test and its
objectives is made, a concise account will be given of
the experimental technique and its anatomical and neuropsychological rationale.

Already in the early 1950s, tachistoscopic viewing
appeared in the psycholinguistic literature. The method
typically refers to a test situation where a number of
short words are presented either successively or
simultaneously to a subject's left and right visual field
through a box-like instrument (a tachistoscope, see
Kimura, 1973), and the subject is required to recall as
many of the exposed items as possible. As a rule, more
words are identified from the right visual field than
from the left. This perceptual asymmetry was originally
explained as caused solely by certain reading habits on
the part of the subjects (i.e. left-to-right scanning,
e.g. Mishkin & Forgays, 1952; Heron, 1957), but with the
development of dichotic listening a decade later, it
became increasingly clear that the tachistoscopic test
results bore a significant relation to the concept of
cerebral dominance as well. Closer scrutiny of the
technique then revealed that in simultaneous, competitive
presentation (two words at a time, one in each visual
field), the effect of cerebral lateralization was often
overridden by the influence of unilateral attention or
ocular scanning movements, whereas in the case of
successive presentation (one word at a time in either the
left or the right visual field), hemispheric specialization
could be measured with significantly less disturbance, as
this form of exposure involves one item only and therefore
a substantially shorter space to be scanned at each time
(cf. Harcum & Finkel, 1963; Overton & Wiener, 1966).
For this reason, the successive (monotic) tachistoscopic
test appears to be an appropriate method in the present

context.

Kimura (1961a; 1966) proposed a neurological explanation of the tachistoscopic effect analogous to that previously outlined for the dichotic listening paradigm (see p. 27 f.). She noted that the afferent optic nerves are crossed, not from each eye to the opposite half of the brain, but from each half of the total visual field to the contralateral cerebral hemisphere. Vision to the left of a central fixation-point is received by the right hemi-retinas of the eyes and projected directly to the visual cortex of the right hemisphere via a contralateral (left eye) and an ipsilateral pathway (right eye), while for vision to the right, the reverse is true, with direct projection to the visual cortex of the left hemisphere (see Figure 5). To explain the superior accuracy of the right visual field in identification of verbal material, Kimura referred to the fact that this field is directly connected to the language-dominant left hemisphere, whereas left-field input is subject to an additional transfer from the right to the left side of the brain via the corpus callosum to reach that hemisphere. Thus, although there still might be a subsidiary effect of reading habits (cf. Overton & Wiener, 1966; White, 1973), this difference of direct and indirect access to the left hemisphere seems to be mainly responsible for the typical advantage of the right visual field in tachistoscopic language experiments.

Like the dichotic listening test, the tachistoscopic viewing procedure has subsequently been verified as a fairly reliable measure of cerebral lateralization, both concerning direction and degree of asymmetry (e.g. Bryden, 1965; Barton et al., 1965; Kershner & Jeng, 1972). As such, many researchers have used it as a primary means for investigating the subtle organization of the human nervous system, or as an important complement to various clinical methods and other experimental approaches within the field of neuropsychology.

The purpose of the present experiment, then, is to investigate the interhemispheric organization of the language-specific lexical systems in Swedish-English

<u>Figure 5</u>

Human brain seen from above. The visual pathways extending
from the eyes to the visual cortices are indicated. The
optic chiasma is the schematic point where the contralateral
optic nerves cross to channel input from the left (broken
line) and the right visual field (continuous line) exclusively
to the opposite hemisphere. (Adapted from Kimura's (1973) model.)

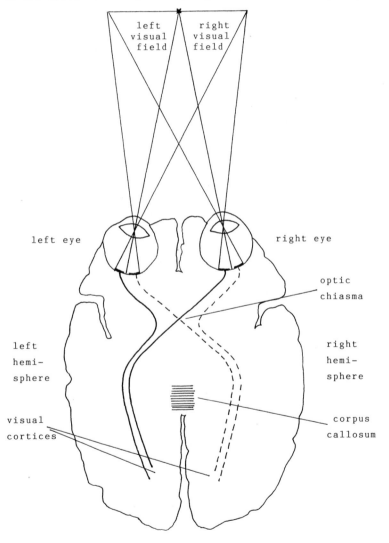

subsidiary bilinguals as measured through visual stimulation.
Specifically, it is of interest to find out if the visual
lateralization patterns match those obtained in the
previous auditory experiment, and if not, what the
differences consist of. In other words, is it reasonable
to distinguish between the notions of auditory and visual
lexical representations in the brain, or should these
denominations be viewed as terminological tools with a
psychological reality only?

To achieve an optimal comparison between our experiments,
the monotic viewing test was designed to parallel the
dichotic listening paradigm as closely as possible.
In fact, apart from the differences of modality and type
of stimulus presentation, the experimental conditions
corresponded entirely in the two tests. Hence, the present
test utilized the same corpus of stimulus words and the
same subject sample as before.

5.1. Hypotheses

The parallelism of test constituents over the experiments
made it possible to employ the same test variables and
hypotheses as before. This is because no significant
differences of recorded lateralization between the auditory
and visual tasks is to be expected a priori, the
fundamental background material (Section 3) being collected
from both types of study. For the reader's convenience,
the working hypotheses of the present experiment are
repeated below.

Hypothesis I: Both the Swedish and the English stimuli
will be processed primarily by the left hemisphere.

Hypothesis II: The English stimuli will engender a
higher degree of left-hemisphere processing than the
Swedish stimuli.

Hypothesis III: There will be no difference of lateralization attributable to the factor of age/English proficiency
level.

Hypothesis IV: Males and females will show equivalent

patterns of left-hemisphere lateralization.

Hypothesis V: Subjects with familial left-handers will exhibit less left-hemisphere lateralization than subjects without such family members.

5.2. Description

Subjects: The subjects were the same as in the dichotic test, i.e. 60 Swedish-English subsidiary bilinguals divided equally into three different age/English proficiency groups with an equal number of males and females in each group. Before the experiment, subjects were given an optic test (Monoyer-Granström's eye chart) to screen out individuals with vision defects, but none of the subjects demonstrated any crucial, uncorrected impairment of their visual ability.[22]

Stimuli: The test battery consisted of the same 60 Swedish and 60 English words as in the previous experiment. The only difference was that the presentation was now visual, and the words were not paired, but exposed one at a time. Within each language, they were divided into discrete six-word blocks composed randomly for each subject by a computer. The words appeared in white uppercase letters (1.0 cm high and .5 cm wide) on a dark background[23], and each item was used twice. Again, then,

---

22. To be more specific, the optic test measured monocular, focal vision, where 1.0 in visual acuity was required for each eye. Although, admittedly, the subsequent tachistoscopic test implicated peripheral rather than focal vision, we used this measure, since there seems to exist a regular covariation between the acuity (but not the perceptual ability) of focal and peripheral vision (e.g. Cornsweet, 1970).

23. The combination of white stimuli and dark background was employed in order to reduce framing effects on the presentation screen, and thereby minimize scanning tendencies that might be specific to a narrowly defined field.

there were 40 blocks of stimuli, 20 in the Swedish test
and 20 in the English (see Appendix).

Apparatus: A BASIC programme for the execution of the
experiment was prepared on a magnetic disc and loaded
into a Heath Z-89 computer. Governed by the programme,
the computer carried out four different routines:
(1) Independent randomization of left and right visual
field words across subjects in both the Swedish and the
English test, (2) independent randomization of the order
of the two tests, (3) presentation of the stimulus words
in both tests, and (4) registration of each subject's
randomization in both tests. Of these, the randomization
routines were included to reduce any effects of stimulus
order in the subsequent results.

The randomization processes were executed by a random-
number generator in the computer, while the presentation
of the stimuli was done on an external Luxor 24" b/w
video screen connected to the computer. An adjustable
chin-rest was used to control the distance between the
subjects' eyes and the screen, and to reduce head
movements.

Responses were written on prefabricated answer forms
similar to those used in the foregoing experiment.

Procedure: All subjects were tested individually in a
quiet, semidarkened room. They sat in front of the video
screen and placed their heads on the chin-rest, which was
individually adjusted to a comfortable height. The
experimenter gave the following instructions viva voce
to each subject in Swedish: "The present experiment is
a visual analogue to the previous auditory test. This
time, you will see words presented successively on the
screen in front of you, and your task is to try to
remember as many of them as possible and subsequently to
write them down. Note that the words will be given one
at a time now and not in pairs as in the auditory test!
The words will be projected at random either to the left
or the right of a central fixation-point, and they will
appear in blocks of six. The exposure time is only a

fraction of a second, so in order to be able to perceive
words on either side, you must concentrate on the fixation-
point. The words will then be seen only in the left or
right periphery of the total visual field, and that is
one of the basic conditions behind the test. You are not
allowed to write anything during a block presentation –
only try to concentrate on the screen and maintain
fixation, this is very important! Try also to avoid
connecting the words with each other, or using other
tricks to remember better – that will only disturb the
effects we are interested in. When you have seen six
words, you are to pick up your pen and write down as many
of them as you can recall. You may write them in any order
you like and you are free to guess when you are uncertain.
There is no time limit – just put down your pen when you
have finished a block and a new block will be presented.
You will be given one Swedish and one English test and
each of these contains 20 blocks."

Since all subjects were familiar with the stimuli from
the preceding experiment[24], no transcript of the language
samples was handed out, but a two-block practice session
was given directly after the instructions. This consisted
of one Swedish and one English block, which were not
included in the test material, and was meant to familiarize
the subjects with the equipment and the testing procedure,
and at the same time ascertain that they had understood
the instructions. After the practice blocks, there was
a short pause, during which the subjects were allowed to
ask questions, if any.

Before the test started, the computer randomized all
the 120 stimulus tokens (2 x 60 words) in each language,

---

24. The lateralization experiments were always run at two
different test sessions separated by at least one day, with
the visual test succeeding the auditory, since it tended
to put higher demands on stimulus perception and therefore
required greater stimulus familiarity. This separation in
time was maintained in order to reduce any priming
(practice) effects of the test material that might obtain
between the experiments.

both sequentially and in terms of left and right side in
relation to the fixation-point, and determined and
displayed the order of the two tests. Each block was
signalled by a warning-tone 4.5 seconds before the first
word appeared and simultaneously the central fixation-point
emerged on the screen. The words were exposed for 100
milliseconds each[25] and had an interstimulus time within
a block of 3.8 seconds. They appeared randomly 4.6 cm
(outer edge) either to the left or the right of the
fixation-point and were constrained to be shown once in
each visual field. Subjects, using binocular viewing[26],
sat at a distance of 60 cm from the screen and the words
thus extended 4.4 degrees horizontally from fixation and
subtended .5 degrees vertically. A mask consisting of a
line of stars covering the postexposural field and with

---

25. The exposure time was set to this particular value
for two reasons: (1) It had to be of shorter duration than
an eye saccade including its preceding stationary movement-
inciting period (about 200 msec), since a fundamental
criterion of the test was that subjects should not have
the time to shift their gaze from the fixation-point onto
the laterally presented word. (2) It had to be brief enough
to prevent perfect performance, as a 100% score would not
allow of any lateral differences. Logically, 50-80%
correct seems to be an appropriate level (cf. p. 41),
and from a series of pilot experiments, the corresponding
exposure time was determined to be approximately 100 msec.

26. Under conditions of binocular viewing, any acuity
differences that may exist between the temporal and nasal
hemifields of one eye or between eyes (Wolf & Gardiner,
1963; Wyke & Chorover, 1965) are expected to balance out
over the left and right visual fields. The effect of eye-
dominance, i.e. the state of one eye being perceptually
superior to the other in terms of more efficient neural
connections, seems in general to be easily overshadowed
by other experimental factors. In fact, no clear-cut
effects from this factor have as yet been demonstrated in
normal binocular tachistoscopic viewing tests (Overton &
Wiener, 1966).

a duration of 100 milliseconds, followed immediately after
each stimulus presentation. This function was introduced
to remove after-images, both on the video screen and on
the retinas of subjects' eyes, in order to limit the
exposure time to its original value.

Each block was triggered by the experimenter, who at
the same time checked from behind that the subjects
followed the instructions. There was a short break
between the Swedish and the English test, and the whole
experiment took approximately 40 minutes.

Scoring: The response data from the tests was manually
corrected by the experimenter using the computer record.
All words correctly recalled and written on the answer
forms were scored as one point. Deviations from this,
such as misspellings, substitutions of phonological
equivalents, or illegible words, were considered as
incorrect responses, yielding nil points (cf. p. 40).

5.3. Results

The test data was worked up statistically in three
different ways: (1) Mean value computations of subjects'
raw scores, (2) summarized individual visual field
asymmetry patterns, and (3) mean value computations of
a laterality index based on the raw scores. Statistics
(analyses of variance) were calculated on two of these
(1 and 3).

The mean raw scores from the present test are given in
Table 4. Evidently, the grand mean score of correctly
identified stimulus words is similar to that of the
auditory test - 33.5 (56%) versus 34.2 (57%) - indicating
that this task too held an appropriate level of difficulty,
i.e. the overall performance was within the 50-80%
interval (cf. p. 41).[27]

---

27. The same hit-rate difference restriction as in the
auditory test was applied here - i.e. no greater difference

As regards incorrect responses, the rate of which
accordingly was 26.5, or 44%, the majority consisted of
blanks as before. The only difference was that the
proportion of unacceptable representations of the stimuli
was somewhat higher in each of the subject groups this
time - 21% overall (cf. p. 41).

Table 4

Mean numbers of correctly reported words in each
experimental condition in the visual test.

	Group A			Group B			Group C			
	M	F	Tot.	M	F	Tot.	M	F	Tot.	Total
Swe. RVF	31.5	33.4	32.4	42.1	36.6	39.3	44.3	42.8	43.5	38.4
Swe. LVF	22.5	23.0	22.7	33.2	29.0	31.1	37.5	36.7	37.1	30.3
Tot. Swe.	27.0	28.2	27.6	37.6	32.8	35.2	40.9	39.7	40.3	34.4
Eng. RVF	27.9	27.9	27.9	36.5	33.5	35.0	43.5	41.5	42.5	35.1
Eng. LVF	21.2	21.3	21.2	33.6	28.7	31.1	38.0	37.3	37.6	30.0
Tot. Eng.	24.5	24.6	24.5	35.0	31.1	33.0	40.7	39.4	40.0	32.5
Grand Tot.	25.8	26.4	26.1	36.3	31.9	34.1	40.8	39.5	40.1	33.4

RVF = right visual field, LVF = left visual field,
M = males, F = females

A four-way analysis of variance with repeated measures
(age/English proficiency level (3) and sex (2) as between-
subject variables and language (2) and visual field (2)
as within-subject variables) was computed on the raw scores
in Table 4.

The following three significant main effects emerged
from the analysis. Age/English proficiency level. The
total mean number of correctly recalled stimulus words
increased with level of age/proficiency, i.e. Group A
had the lowest mean score (26.1), Group B was intermediate (34.1), and Group C had the highest mean score
(40.1), $(F(2,54)=13.5, p<.001)$. Language. More Swedish
than English words were correctly reported (mean numbers =

---

than 50% of the total number of identified words was
allowed between the left and right visual fields.
Again, however, no rejection of response data was
necessary (cf. note 15).

34.4 vs. 32.6), (F(1,54)=7.6, p<.01). <u>Visual field</u>.
Words from the right visual field were identified to
a higher extent than words from the left visual field
(mean numbers = 36.8 vs. 30.2), (F(1,54)=133.2, p<.001).

The sex factor did not yield any significant effect,
but there was a weak tendency for males to surpass
females on the task (mean numbers = 34.4 vs. 32.6),
(F(1,54)=.6, p=.46).

In addition, there was a significant two-way interaction: <u>Language x visual field</u>. The difference of the
mean scores between the right and left visual fields was
greater for Swedish than for English (mean differences =
8.2 vs. 5.1), (F(1,54)=11.8, p<.01). No other interactions reached significance.

Figures were also computed on each individual subject's
potential asymmetry relation between the visual fields.
This was done analogically to the procedure used in the
auditory test, i.e. in terms of the right visual field
being superior to the left (RVFA) or vice versa (LVFA),
or the two fields being equal in accuracy (RVF=LVF).
The summarized scores from this measure are presented in
Table 5. (As before, no statistical analysis was carried
out on this type of data.)

Table 5

Numbers and percentages of subjects with a RVFA, LVFA,
and RVF=LVF in the Swedish and the English part of the
visual test.

	Group A		Group B		Group C		Total	
	number	%	number	%	number	%	number	%
Swe. RVFA	18	90	17	85	18	90	53	88
Swe. RVF=LVF	1	5	1	5	1	5	3	5
Swe. LVFA	1	5	2	10	1	5	4	7
Eng. RVFA	18	90	14	70	17	85	49	82
Eng. RVF=LVF	1	5	2	10	1	5	4	7
Eng. LVFA	1	5	4	20	2	10	7	11

Since the levels of overall performance varied
considerably, both within and between the Swedish and
the English test, the raw scores in Table 4 were trans-

formed to the laterality index (LI) used in the auditory
test (LI = ((R-L)/(R+L))x100) in order to achieve an
unbiased measure of lateralization.[28] In Table 6, the
mean values of the laterality indices are given for
the different experimental conditions.

Table 6

Mean values of the laterality index in the different
experimental conditions in the visual test.

	Group A			Group B			Group C			
	M	F	Tot.	M	F	Tot.	M	F	Tot.	Total
Swe. LI	18.0	20.5	19.2	13.7	15.4	14.5	8.8	8.4	8.6	14.1
Eng. LI	15.5	14.2	14.8	6.6	9.7	8.2	7.1	6.3	6.7	9.9
Total LI	16.7	17.4	17.0	10.2	12.6	11.4	8.0	7.4	7.7	12.0

Obviously, all experimental conditions yielded a
substantial right visual field advantage (LI>0). If the
laterality indices are plotted as a function of age/English
proficiency level for males and females in the Swedish and
English tests, the following two figures evolve.

Figure 6

Laterality for males and females as a function of age/English
proficiency level in the Swedish part of the visual test.

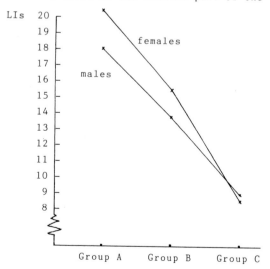

Figure 7

Laterality for males and females as a function of age/English proficiency level in the English part of the visual test.

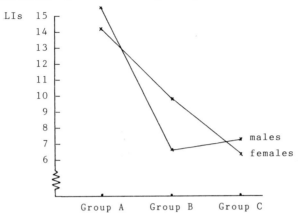

To achieve a more general picture of the trends within the LI-data, we collapse the scores across sex and let them merge into a single graph.

Figure 8

Laterality as a function of age/English proficiency level in the Swedish and the English part of the visual test.

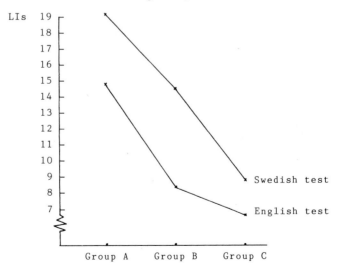

From the last graph, we can see that the pattern of
laterality is similar to that received in the auditory
test. English words again seem to yield less lateralization
than Swedish ones, and there also tends to be a general
decrease of lateralization as the age/proficiency level
increases. The between-group relation of LI-differences
between the languages has, however, changed - now the
greatest divergence is found in Group A (4.4) and
Group B (6.3), while Group C exhibits only a small
difference (1.9).

A three-way analysis of variance with repeated
measures (age/English proficiency level (3), sex (2),
and language (2)) was conducted on the laterality
indices to test the reliability of the observed differences.
Two significant main effects emerged from this treatment:
Age/English proficiency level. The value of the laterality
index diminished as the level of age/proficiency increased,
i.e. Group A had a mean index of 17.0, Group B 11.4, and
Group C 7.7, $(F(2,54)=5.1, p<.01)$. Language. The laterality
indices were generally higher for the Swedish material
than for the English (mean values = 14.1 vs. 9.9),
$(F(1,54)=7.6, p<.01)$.

Neither the influence of sex (male LI = 11.6, female
LI = 12.6) nor any of the possible interactions involving
this factor or any other factors approached significance.

A correlation test was also carried out on the Swedish
and English LIs to investigate whether a visual field
effect in one language was related to such an effect in
the other language. A significant r = .48 (p<.001) was
the result, arguing for a rather high correlation of the
laterality indices in the individual subjects.

---

28. A post hoc correlation test on the laterality indices
and their corresponding total raw scores (R+L) revealed
that both the Swedish and the English indices covaried
with overall performance (r = -.63, p<.001 and r = -.60,
p<.001, respectively). The visual LIs thus seem to be
more related to overall performance than the auditory
ones reported before (Swedish r = -.36 and English r =
-.24, cf. notes 19 and 34).

Finally, the possible influence of familial handedness on the LIs was tested in a separate three-way analysis of variance with repeated measures (familial handedness (2), language (2), and visual field (2)). Although a substantial difference of mean values was found (subjects with familial left-handers = 16.6 vs. such without =7.4), no significant main effect emerged (F(1,58)=.4, p=.50), nor were there any significant interactions.

5.4. Discussion

It is evident from the present results that there is a significant advantage for the identification of both Swedish and English words in the right visual field of our bilingual subjects (<u>visual field</u> - raw scores; cf. Tables 4, 5, and 6). Presumably, this effect is due to an asymmetrical underlying neuropsychological organization, where both languages are subserved somewhat more by the left hemisphere. Such an outcome is well in accordance with previous research on cerebral dominance in bilinguals, as well as with the results of our foregoing dichotic listening experiment, and accordingly the prediction of Hypothesis I is confirmed anew.

In contrast to the auditory test, however, the visual investigation yielded significant differences also <u>within</u> the general pattern of left-hemisphere dominance. A priori, we predicted that English words (acquired formally) would induce a higher degree of left-hemisphere processing than Swedish ones (acquired informally), since the majority of earlier studies imply this state of affairs (Hypothesis II). It is therefore rather remarkable to find that the present test engendered a significant difference in the opposite direction, i.e. that the material associated with formal acquisition evoked less left-lateralization than that connected with formal acquisition (<u>language</u> - LIs; cf. <u>language x visual field</u> - raw scores). As this upshot was hinted at already in the auditory test, although not being statistically reliable

there, it has now become apparent that the prediction of
Hypothesis II is not valid for our sample of bilinguals.
Other or additional factors seem to be at work in
conditioning the hemispheric patterns for Swedish and
English lexical processing. However, notwithstanding the
comparatively greater laterality difference between the
languages in the visual test, there was still a substantial
interlingual correlation of the index data ($r = .48$; cf.
auditory $r = .53$) in the individual subjects. Again, then,
the magnitude (or lack) of a hemispheric advantage in one
language appears to entail a similar state in the other
language.

Regarding the different subject groups, a significant
decrease of left-hemisphere dominance with increasing
age/English proficiency level was recorded in both
languages (<u>age/English proficiency level</u> - LIs). This
result is in conflict with Hypothesis III, which forecast
that there would be no laterality difference attributable
to the factor of age/proficiency, but rather that the
patterns of hemispheric processing would be approximately
equal for the three groups. Since the present findings are
tentatively supported by a similar, but weaker and
insignificant trend in the auditory test, it seems
necessary to reject also Hypothesis III, and look for
alternative, a posteriori explanations for the results
obtained.

Lastly, in accordance with the auditory test, neither
of the between-subject factors sex and familial handedness
engendered any significant differences of lateralization.
As expected, a rough parallelism of hemispheric asymmetry
between males and females was demonstrated, which thus
validates the predicted lack of effect of the sex factor
also through the visual modality (Hypothesis IV). Similarly,
the previous approximate equivalence of lateralization
between subjects with and without familial left-handers
was repeated, but as this finding contradicts the idea
of Hypothesis V, i.e. that the former group would show less
pronounced lateralization than the latter, a revision either
of the importance of this factor in hemispheric organization
or of our experimental methods and results now looks

inevitable. (For a more extensive discussion of the present findings, see Section 6.2).

6. Auditory and visual tests combined

In the following section, we will combine the results of the auditory and visual tests in order to attain a unitary picture of the findings of our lateralization inquiries. These data will then be used in a tentative appraisal of the hemispheric organization of the bilingual lexical system, including some speculative explanations of the trends obtained.

6.1. Results

The combined figures will be reported in a way analogous to the corresponding sections in the auditory and visual tests. In Table 7, the conjoined mean raw scores are given.

Table 7

Mean numbers of correctly reported words in each experimental condition of the auditory and visual tests combined.

	Group A M	F	Tot.	Group B M	F	Tot.	Group C M	F	Tot.	Total
Swe. RS	34.3	35.8	35.0	41.7	37.5	39.6	43.6	42.4	43.0	39.2
Swe. LS	25.4	28.2	26.8	35.1	30.6	32.8	37.6	37.7	37.6	32.4
Tot. Swe.	29.9	32.0	30.9	38.4	34.1	36.2	40.6	40.1	40.3	35.8
Eng. RS	28.3	27.8	28.0	36.8	32.4	34.6	41.3	37.3	39.3	34.0
Eng. LS	22.0	22.3	22.1	34.4	27.6	31.0	36.4	35.3	35.8	29.6
Tot. Eng.	25.1	25.1	25.1	35.6	30.0	32.8	38.9	36.3	37.6	31.8
Grand Tot.	27.5	28.5	28.0	37.0	32.0	34.5	39.7	38.2	39.0	33.8

RS = right side (ear/visual field), LS = left side (ear/visual field), M = males, F = females

An overall five-way analysis of variance with repeated measures (age/English proficiency level (3), sex (2), language (2), side - i.e. ear/visual field - (2), and experiment - i.e. auditory versus visual perception - (2)) on the data in Table 7 gave the following three significant main effects. Age/English proficiency level, ($F(2,54)=$ 18.4, p<.001). Language, ($F(1,54)=86.0$, p<.001). Side, ($F(1,54)=116.7$, p<.001). Since these effects were significant in each of the two experiments as well, no additional comment is needed here.

There were, however, also no less than six significant two-way interactions, of which three pertain to the newly introduced experiment variable: Language x age/English proficiency level. The difference between the Swedish and the English raw scores declined as the age/proficiency level increased, i.e. Group A had a mean difference of 5.8, Group B 3.4, and Group C 2.7, ($F(2,54)=4.7$, p<.05). In the preceding separate analyses, a similar significant interaction was seen in the auditory test, while the effect in the visual test was insignificant. Experiment x age/English proficiency level. Group A scored higher on the auditory test than on the visual (mean scores = 30.0 vs. 26.1), whereas the reverse was true for Group C (mean scores = 37.7 vs. 40.1), with Group B falling in-between (mean scores = 34.9 vs. 34.1), ($F(2,54)=3.3$, p<.05). Language x sex. Females exhibited a greater difference between the languages than did males (mean differences = 4.9 vs. 3.1), ($F(1,54)=4.8$, p<.05). Previously, this relationship was found to be significant in the auditory test, but not in the visual. Side x language. The left-right difference was greater for Swedish than for English (mean differences = 6.7 vs. 4.3), ($F(1,54)=13.9$, p<.001). Contrary to the preceding inter-action, this effect was found in the visual test only, and not in the auditory in the previous separate analyses. Experiment x language. Swedish words were better heard than seen, i.e. the auditory test scores were higher than the visual for this language (mean scores = 37.3 vs. 34.4), while the opposite pattern applied to the English words, which were better seen than heard, i.e. the visual test

scores were higher than the auditory for this language
(mean scores = 32.5 vs. 31.1), (F(1,54)=22.2, p<.001).
Side x experiment. The left-right difference was greater
for the visual test than for the auditory (mean
differences = 6.6 vs. 4.5), (F(1,54)=5.5, p<.05). No
other interactions reached significance.

Further, the scores in Table 7 indicate that the criteria
used for selecting the test population were effective. When
the project was initially designed, great pains were taken
to find subjects who conformed to all the experimental pre-
requisites, for example that they should be native speakers
of Swedish with English as a foreign language (subsidiary
bilinguals), where English was mastered up to one of three
different predetermined proficiency levels (see p. 33).
As is natural, the Swedish test yielded a higher mean score
than the English (35.8 vs. 31.8), since subjects normally
are more proficient in their native language and hence
perform better than in the foreign language. Correspondingly,
the division into different proficiency groups is justified
by there being a proportional increment of mean score as
the hypothesized proficiency level increased, i.e. Group A
had 28.8, Group B 34.5, and Group C 39.0.

If the combined data is listed in terms of each
individual subject's potential left-right asymmetry
relation between the ears/visual fields, the scores in
Table 8 obtain. (Again, no statistics were performed on
this type of data.)

Table 8

Numbers and percentages of instances of a right side advantage (RSA), a left side advantage (LSA), and equality between
the sides (RS=LS) in the auditory and visual tests combined.

	Group A number	%	Group B number	%	Group C number	%	Total number	%
Swe. RSA	35	88	31	78	33	83	99	82
Swe. RS=LS	2	5	3	7	3	7	8	7
Swe. LSA	3	7	6	15	4	10	13	11
Eng. RSA	32	80	25	62	29	72	86	72
Eng. RS=LS	3	7	5	13	1	3	9	7
Eng. LSA	5	13	10	25	10	25	25	21

A combined comparison of the laterality indices derived
from the two experiments was also made. In Table 9, the
mean values of the pooled LIs are given.

Table 9

Mean values of the laterality index in the different
experimental conditions of the auditory and visual tests
combined.

	Group A			Group B			Group C			
	M	F	Tot.	M	F	Tot.	M	F	Tot.	Total
Swe. LI	16.2	13.3	14.7	9.4	12.6	11.0	8.0	6.1	7.0	10.9
Eng. LI	13.8	11.4	12.6	4.5	9.4	7.0	6.7	3.1	4.9	8.2
Total LI	15.0	12.4	13.7	7.0	11.0	9.0	7.4	4.7	6.0	9.6

The usual graphic transformations of the main LI-data
yield the following figures for the pooled scores.

Figure 9

Laterality for males and females as a function of
age/English proficiency level in the Swedish parts of the
auditory and visual tests combined.

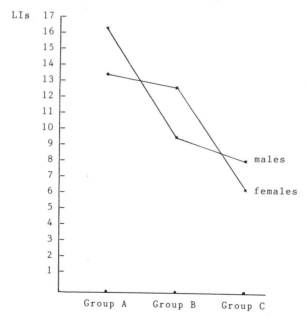

Figure 10

Laterality for males and females as a function of
age/English proficiency level in the English parts of
the auditory and visual tests combined

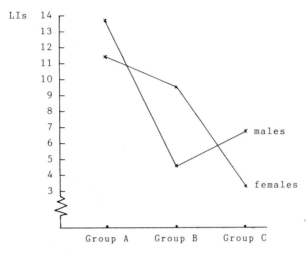

Figure 11

Laterality collapsed across sex as a function of
age/English proficiency level in the Swedish and English
parts of the auditory and visual tests combined.

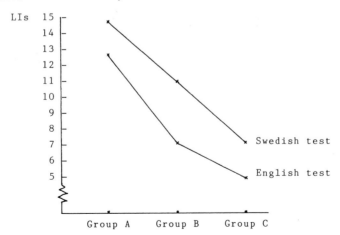

As can be seen, the combined measure of indexed
laterality yields roughly parallel curves for the lateral
advantages of Swedish and English lexical stimuli. The
declining trend over age/English proficiency level is
easily perceived, as is the differential magnitude of LI
for the two languages, and the within-group laterality
differences of language now seem to be of a similar
size (Group A = 2.1, Group B = 4.0, and Group C = 2.1).

The reliability of the observed tendencies was tested
in a four-way analysis of variance with repeated measures
(age/English proficiency level (3), sex (2), language (2),
and experiment (2)). This treatment revealed three
significant main effects: Age/English proficiency level.
The mean value of the laterality index decreased with
increasing level of age/proficiency, i.e. Group A had a
mean LI of 13.7, Group B 9.0, and Group C 6.0, $(F(2,54)=$
5.8, p<.01). While this effect previously was significant
in the visual test only, the present combined analysis
produced a high reliability score for the influence of
this factor. Language. The LIs in the Swedish tests were
generally higher than those in the English tests (mean
values = 10.9 vs. 8.2), $(F(1,54)=7.2$, p<.01). Again, then,
the combined analysis brought a significant effect in the
visual test together with an insignificant one in the
auditory test substantially beyond the crucial probability
level. Experiment. The visual test resulted in higher
values of the laterality index than did the auditory one
(mean values = 12.0 vs. 7.1), $(F(1,54)=8.2$, p<.01).

The fourth factor, sex, displayed an approximate
equivalence of lateralization between males and females
(mean values = 9.8 vs. 9.4), and was accordingly far from
being significantly influential $(F(1,54)=.05$, p=.82).

None of the potential interactions in the data reached
significance. Near this level were an experiment x
language interaction $(F(1,54)=1.4$, p=.24) and a sex x
age/English proficiency level interaction $(F(2,54)=1.5$,
p=.24).

Besides, two correlation tests were computed on the
LI-data. On the one hand, the relationship between the
Swedish and English results pooled over experiment was

tested, in which a strong interlingual covariation of
lateral advantages was found (r = .60, p<.001). On the
other hand, the scores from the two experiments pooled
over language were compared, but here the correlation
fell short of significance (r = .17, p=.19). Thus, the
lateral effects of language seem to be closely related
in the individual subjects, while there obviously is a
great deal of individual variation between the test
methods.

Finally, no combined analysis of variance on familial
handedness was considered necessary to carry out, as
neither of the separate tests had even approached any
significant effects of this factor (cf. auditory F-value =
.1, p=.73, visual F-value = .4, p=.50).

6.2. General discussion

With the combined results of our lateralization study
in hand, there are four important findings which warrant
further discussion, viz. the effects of side (raw scores),
language (LIs), age/English proficiency level (LIs), and
experiment (LIs). In addition, the apparent lack of
influence from sex and familial handedness in this
context needs some clarification as well.

Interhemispheric relations: The amalgamated scores for
word identification in the auditory and visual modalities
gave a strong advantage for the right ear/visual field
irrespective of language in our test population (side -
raw scores). As pointed out before, the consensus of
opinion is that this asymmetry reflects the dominance of
the left cerebral hemisphere in processing verbal material,
and in particular lexical stimuli, since there is a high
correlation between this type of data and various clinical
measures of language impairment following unilateral
brain damage (e.g. Albert & Obler, 1978; Paradis, 1977).
Although other explanations of the effect cannot be ruled
out completely (cf. Blumstein et al., 1975; Hines & Satz,

1974; Colbourn, 1978), a neurological connection seems
to make most sense, and we will therefore make this
explanation the foundation of our further discussion.

It thus seems reasonably clear that most of our
bilinguals display some left-lateralization for the
lexical functions tested, but what does this concept of
dominance actually mean? Should lateralization be viewed
as a defined anatomical phenomenon, where the neural
representation of the words an individual has acquired
(a combined structural and semantic memory) is stored
in a localizable portion of the cerebral cortex,
primarily the left? Or is it rather a question of
different perceptuocognitive processes - most of which
are better handled by the left hemisphere - that are
selectively activated by the type of stimulus and task,
and where the neural basis of the lexical system
per se is a function of virtually all the cells in the
brain?

It is impossible to give a clear-cut answer to this
question presently, but there are certain indications
as to the most plausible solution. It has been shown
that certain specific neural structures in the left
hemisphere are significantly larger (almost one third
in relative terms) than the corresponding area in the
right hemisphere in about 65% of the investigated cases[29].
This asymmetry seems to be true in both adults
(Geschwind & Levitsky, 1968) and infants (Witelson &
Pallie, 1973). The region concerned (the left planum
temporale) is situated in the superior part of the
temporal lobe, a portion of the cortex which is
associated with auditory comprehension, and in particular
with word-processing mechanisms, since in case of damage
to this area, sensory (Wernicke's) aphasia is the typical
result, with disturbances of the ability to couple
lexical surface forms with their underlying semantic
concepts as the salient feature (e.g. Hécaen, 1969;
Boller et al., 1977). Incidentally, we thereby seem to

---

29. In fact, Wada et al. (1975) have reported that these
structures may be absent altogether in the right hemisphere.

have identified a crucial area for the functioning of the
internal lexicon seen from an intrahemispheric viewpoint.
These findings suggest that there is an anatomical
differentiation of the brain in favour of the left hemisphere, which probably is genetically preprogrammed, since
it appears to be present, wholly or partially, already at
birth. As its estimated incidence of occurrence tallies
quite well with different measurements of receptive
lexical lateralization, including the present (about 75%),
it is tempting to connect this structural bias with the
left-lateralized lexical system, although the evidence is
far from conclusive on this point (cf. p. 13).

If we accept this position, however, we still have to
determine whether the anatomical preponderance of the left
hemisphere is the consequence of material specificity or
process specificity, or perhaps a combination of both
(e.g. Bogen, 1969). Evidence from aphasiology has often
favoured the localizationist view (linguistic modality-
or stratum-specific subcenters in the brain, e.g. separate
auditory and visual "lexicons" or separate lexical and
grammatical systems), since different types of aphasic
syndromes have implied a rather direct link between
verbal function and topographically defined portions of
the cerebral cortex (although not being applied in the
narrow sense in modern times, see e.g. Dingwall & Whitaker,
1974), but with the development of current experimental
techniques, a gradual shift towards a left-right
difference in terms of more general processing strategies
has occurred (cf. p. 14). This transition is mirrored in
several recent studies, where lateralization patterns
have been found to vary significantly according to the
type of processing required, e.g. conditioned by type
of stimuli (e.g. Rogers et al., 1977), task difficulty
(e.g. Satz et al., 1968), and mode of response (e.g.
Galloway, 1983). In addition, the present view may also
reflect an increasing ambition among researchers to
lessen the disturbing discrepancy between recorded
anatomical and functional data in general.

However, the process specificity hypothesis alone
cannot account sufficiently for the findings from aphasia,

at least not in its overall sense, since there are
specific language (lexical) symptoms, e.g. certain
decoding or memory deficits, which do not obtain in
other types of cognitive functioning. This selectivity
may be observed in cases of sensory aphasia, where the
disturbances affect primarily comprehension and storage
of lexical items. Although he has a verbal deficit, the
aphasic patient does not necessarily suffer impairment
of his ability to decode non-lexical information or to
memorize or recall such material (cf. Luria, 1970;
Critchley, 1970).

In the light of this, as well as of other discussions
on the topic (e.g. Albert & Obler, 1978; Vaid & Genesee,
1980), the most realistic theory of lateralization seems
to be a synthesis of material and processing specialization
in the brain, where a whole hierarchy of neuropsychological
levels are implicated. The dominance of the left hemisphere
would then be dependent upon a series of increasingly
complex constituents, ranging from base-level neural
storage of lexical data, via certain language-specific
subprocesses, to general, hemispherically specialized
modes of processing. Irrespective of anatomical differences,
such a compromise appears to match the empirical data from
different fields of research most accurately.

Returning to the findings from our experiments, there
thus seems to be a comparatively profound and stable
effect of left-hemisphere dominance in the data. But what
about the more subtle, subsidiary effects within this
gross trend of lateralization? Are the demonstrated
within-group and between-group differences of indexed
laterality similarly represented in terms of neurophysiological organization, or are they rather simply
a function of more superficial processing strategies
conditioned by the selection of subjects, stimuli, and
test method?

Interlingual relations: If we start with the language
effect, the combined analysis gave a significantly higher
right side/left hemisphere advantage for Swedish words as
compared to English (language - LIs; cf. side x language -

raw scores). This result implies a partial dissociation
of the Swedish and English lexical processing mechanisms
over the hemispheres, where the informally acquired L1
would be somewhat more amenable to left-hemisphere
treatment than the formally acquired L2. The puzzle
with this conclusion, however, is that it is apparently
not in concord with the majority of previous studies on
bilingual lateralization, which have indicated an opposite
relation between formal and informal language backgrounds,
with greater left-dominance for L2 than L1. It seems
necessary therefore to analyze both earlier material and
the present data somewhat more closely.

   What one is first struck by, is the diversity of
languages involved in the background studies. Out of 13
reported investigations, at least eight implicated
languages which differ in terms of the language-specific
variables discussed in Section 3. Different organizational
effects from these may well have contributed to the predominant pattern L1<L2, let alone the possible influence
of other, procedural differences. Of the five remaining
studies, two more seem dubious in the present context,
since one involved small samples of many different
combinations of linguistically similar and dissimilar
languages, and the other did not refer to the distinction
between formal and informal language acquisition in the
strict sense (see Galloway, 1983). The three remaining
lateralization investigations, however, which are
comparable to the present regarding both intralinguistic
similarity and distinction of language acquisition, give
a novel and suggestive picture of the problem - two
(Maitre, 1974; Schneiderman & Wesche, 1983) indicate
L1>L2, whereas only one (Carroll, 1980) yields the original
L1<L2. Thus, by applying more stringent restrictions on
the background data, we arrive at a reverse relation
between the languages, agreeing more with the findings
from the present experiment.

   The implications of this trend must not be exaggerated,
though, since there are only two supportive studies.
Rather, it serves to illustrate the ease with which a
reversal may be procured. Interlingual lateralization

patterns seem to be quite sensitive to a number of background and procedural factors, some of which are only
weakly related to cerebral organization, and the way
the pendulum will swing may often be determined by
extraneous influence from selectively applied methods
and constituents of study. If different factors are
emphasized or neglected, it is possible to end up in
either position of the moot point, a fact which probably
accounts for a great deal of conflicting evidence in
this realm.

On the basis of what is said above, we will argue
that most languages are equally lateralized to the left
hemisphere as regards the deeper, neurophysiological
processes of verbal storage and function. This component
of lateralization would be the major one, where its
direction and magnitude, determined by genetic predisposition, is relatively invariable in the healthy
individual[30] (cf. Kinsbourne & Hiscock, 1977; Witelson,
1977). The significant differences of language laterality
which have been recorded in many studies, including the
present, should rather be viewed as a reflection of
certain variable, superficial processing mechanisms
educed by a combination of background and procedural
factors. Though such a proposal might seem controversial,
it fits the results of previous research best.

First, as we have seen, clinical data from aphasia
advocate parallel organization of the languages in
bilinguals (see Section 1), and so do also experimental
findings if they are pooled over different types of
investigation and averaged (cf. $((L1>L2)+(L1=L2)+(L1<L2))/3=$
$(L1=L2)$; see p. 12). Second, recent clinical work using
the more direct measures of cortical stimulation and
sodium amytal tests have spoken against any hemispheric
differences between the languages. Instead, as L2 is
acquired, a certain modification of the neural organization

---

30. A shift of hemispheric dominance for language may,
however, occur in brain-damaged children during the
initial years of "cerebral plasticity" (e.g. Krashen,
1973; Lenneberg, 1967).

within the left hemisphere seems to take place, where a
larger area of this hemisphere is utilized to house and
process the data from the additional language (Ojemann &
Whitaker, 1978; Rapport et al., 1980). Third, the
variability of experimental results over background
and procedural factors has been empirically demonstrated
in several studies (e.g. Bryden, 1965; Blumstein et al.,
1975; cf. Obler et al., 1982). Taken together, these
three sources of evidence make a cogent argument in
favour of the present theory.

But how, then, do the results from our experiments
conform to this organizational framework? First of all,
there seems to exist a substantial hemispheric parallelism
between the Swedish and English lexical representations
as indicated by the high interlingual correlation of
the LIs ($r = .60$, $p < .001$). This implies that despite
some heterogeneity in the data, there is a basic, deep-
level interdependence of the languages in the brain.
In other words, if one language for whatever reason
exhibits a strong or weak lateralization, or even
bilaterality, we can be almost sure that the other is
distributed more or less similarly. The putative neurophysiological explanation of this covariation is that
L1 and L2 utilize the same, or similar, neural mechanisms,
at least as seen from a left-right perspective. What the
intrahemispheric implications might be is beyond the
theme of this discussion, but to find language-specific
structures anywhere in the cerebral cortex, it is
probably necessary to go down to the microscopic level
(cf. Whitaker, 1978).

Further, the differential laterality effects of
language that still obtain may be explained in terms
of more superficial processing patterns. If we take the
demonstrated experiment x language (raw scores) as our
starting-point, an interesting performance difference
emerges. When Swedish words were dealt with, the auditory
test gave higher scores than the visual, but when it was
a question of English words, the reverse was true, with
better identification in the visual test than in the
auditory. This pattern is well in accordance with our

postulated distinction of formal and informal language
acquisition, where Swedish is viewed as being acquired
primarily through the auditory modality and English
through the visual (cf. p. 20). Hence, there is an
empirically substantiated correlation between L1 and
auditory processing and L2 and visual processing
respectively.

A possible factor behind this modality distinction
is also the degree of sound-to-symbol correspondence in
each of the languages. In studies of aphasia, it has been
shown that languages with regular correspondences between
pronunciation and spelling are more tied to auditory
processing than languages with less regular relationships,
which instead exhibit stronger connections with visual
processing (e.g. Luria, 1960; Peuser & Leischner, 1974).
As Swedish has a more rigorous sound-to-symbol correspondence
than English, this factor may amplify the discrete effects
of the two acquisitional modes.

We have already seen that with narrow restrictions on
test and background factors, lower laterality is indicated
for formally acquired languages than informally acquired
ones (p. 77). Admittedly, this evidence is weak, but we
may eke it out by connecting our acquisitional distinction
with that of early and late bilinguals, and thereby attain
a somewhat firmer footing. Early bilinguals (simultaneous
acquisition) typically rely on informal methods of learning
irrespective of language, whereas late bilinguals often
differ in this respect, with a more formal approach to L2
in contrast to the informally acquired L1. This generalization may be made, since by definition early bilinguals are
seen as having acquired both languages before they have
developed any sophisticated abstractive or metalinguistic
ability in dealing with verbal material (characteristic
of formal learning), and in consequence, instances of
formal L2-acquisition should belong to the category of
late bilinguals.

In Section 3, we reviewed a number of studies pertaining to the factor of age of acquiring L2, which
either referred to early or late bilinguals, or both.
As our subjects were exclusively late bilinguals (in the

early range though), we may leave the data from early
bilinguals aside, and focus on those individuals who
commenced L2-learning at the age of 10 or later. In
Table 10, the findings from these studies are given in
terms of type of lateralization pattern evoked, and
required level and type of processing in carrying out
the respective probe tasks.[31] The interlingual patterns
are grouped as supportive and non-supportive depending
on their relation to the results from our experiments
(L1>L2), and the level of processing is defined, in
accordance with the criteria put forward by Galloway
(1983), as deep if it requires elaborate linguistic
operations, i.e. semantic processing of the stimuli
(comprehension), and superficial if it does not, i.e.
simple perception-reproduction of a visual or auditory
code.

Table 10

Number of studies espousing and contradicting the left-
hemisphere lateralization pattern L1>L2 divided in terms
of required level and type of neuropsychological processing
in the different test paradigms.

		L1>L2?		
		yes	no	yes+no
deep processing	auditory	2	5	
	visual	1	2	10
	subtotal	3	7	
superficial processing	auditory	2	0	
	visual	4	0	6
	subtotal	6	0	
	Total	9	7	16

Evidently, there is a slight advantage (nine vs. seven
studies) for the pattern L1>L2 in late bilinguals, not
taking other variables into account. This overall trend is

---

31. Only those studies which explicitly referred to the
present issue (16 out of 18) are included in the data in
Table 10.

not altogether unheard-of, since it has been suggested
on sundry occasions before (e.g. Vaid & Genesee, 1980;
Genesee, 1982), as well as being anticipated through our
distinction of formal and informal L2-acquisition. But
if we break the data down into different processing
types, an intriguing interaction between test conditions
and results evolves.

First, deep and superficial tests produce different
results. If semantic processing is not a prerequisite
for executing the task - i.e. both superficial and deep
processing are possible - unequivocal support (six vs.
nil studies) is adduced for differential lateralization
of the languages, with L1>L2. On the other hand, if
analysis of meaning is required - i.e. deep processing
is possible only - the picture is changed, with the
majority of studies (seven vs. three) indicating rough
parallelism between the languages, L1=L2. Second, the
distinction between deep and superficial processing
obviously covaries with modality of stimulus presenta-
tion/processing. Deep tests seem to consist primarily of
auditory methods (seven vs. three), while superficial
tests rather implicate visual procedures (four vs. two).

These findings thus bring us full circle back to the
starting-point of our argument - the distinction between
auditory and visual processing. Although the reasoning
in no way claims to be conclusive, neuropsychological
functioning being too complex a problem to allow of any
simple, unidimensional solutions, a few good points may
be made in favour of differential processing strategies
as the main factor behind our experimental results.

The basic difference of age and manner of acquisition
between L1 and L2, and possibly also the subsidiary effect
of interlingual differences in terms of sound-to-symbol
correspondence, semm to have engendered as one of their
products a modality distinction, where Swedish stimuli
are slightly more amenable to auditory decoding and
English stimuli conversely to visual treatment.[32] This

---

32. The auditory-visual distinction over the languages is
also supported by data from individuals' general neuro-

difference is probably related to level of processing,
and in particular to how much analysis of meaning is
carried out. Theoretically, no semantic processing is
necessary to accomplish a dichotic listening or monotic
viewing task, there being no requirement of actually
having understood the presented words, but still there
is apparently a great deal of meaning analysis performed
in such tests (cf. auditory and visual Stroop tests, e.g.
Hamers & Lambert, 1972; Preston & Lambert, 1969). In
other words, our tests did not necessitate any specific
level of processing, but semantic and structural analysis
may have been used to different extents in the two
languages by different individuals.

If semantic decoding is a crucial facet of auditory
processing, as in fact is suggested by Galloway & Scarcella
(1982), and its importance in visual analyses is less
pronounced, this may explain why Swedish, more dependent
on auditory processing, appeared more lateralized than
English, more dependent on visual processing (cf. Lambert &
Rawlings, 1969; Genesee et al., 1978). Support for this
idea is also adduced from another perspective by Hines
(1976; 1977), whose lateralization studies indicated that
auditory perception-visual reproduction involves more
semantic processing than visual-visual procedures. One
must be aware, however, that the distinction is arguably
rather fine in our material, since the recorded laterality
difference it is thought to have contributed to is
relatively small (10.9 vs. 8.2 in index figures).

From these observations, we can deduce that our

---

physiological development. Whitaker (1978), for example,
has claimed that the cortical regions which subserve
visual functions (the supramarginal and angular gyri)
tend to mature considerably later than other regions in
the brain, for example those controlling auditory functions.
This difference probably coincided with the present
successive mode of language acquisition in such a way
that our subjects possessed relatively more auditory, or
less visual, abilities when they acquired L1 than when
they acquired L2.

hypothesized modes of processing are correlated with age
and manner of language acquisition. The typically early
and informal contact with Swedish seems to have generated
a semantic or deep-level type of analysis of these words,
which is carried out to a substantial extent by the left
hemisphere. On the other hand, the later and more formal
contact with English has presumably induced a somewhat
more code-based or superficial pattern of analysis, where
the left-hemisphere dominance is less emphasized.

This semantic-structural processing distinction is of
course not a new-fledged idea - on the contrary, it has
been in the air for quite some time in terms of the
levels-of-processing theory (e.g. Craik & Lockhart, 1972).
There is ample evidence in the literature that different
processing levels exist in mind and that the depth or
superficiality of processing is dependent on various
factors, for example test instructions, task complexity,
and stimulus type (e.g. Hyde & Jenkins, 1973; Craik &
Tulving, 1975; Cermak & Craik, 1979). (Cf. also the
distinction between primary and secondary memory processing, e.g. Waugh & Norman, 1965.)

If level of processing reflects an individual's
experience of language as outlined above, the differences
in laterality that we have observed seem quite natural.
It is to be expected that the differential cognitive
conditions behind the acquisition of L1 and L2 will
almost certainly have some neuropsychological repercussions
on the way these languages are internalized and used.
For example, the degree of cognitive maturity is
enormously enhanced from the two- or three-year-old
acquiring L1 to the 10-year-old acquiring L2, a difference
which may be presumed to influence the level of linguistic
consciousness and abstraction ability in language processing (e.g. Hatch, 1977; Whitaker, 1978).

Another factor is previous language experience.
Whereas the infant's brain is more or less like a tabula
rasa semantically when L1 is acquired, the 10-year-old
has the convenience of being able to draw on the semantic
network of L1 when learning L2. These effects add to the
plausibility of our theory - when L1 was acquired, a

working semantic system had to be established con-
comitantly to store the meaning of the different lexical
items that were learnt. The connections between surface
and deep forms of words in this language would thus be
particularly closely connected. When L2 was internalized,
on the other hand, these connections might have become
less marked, because the acquirer was often prone to
process some aspects of it through his native language
system - i.e. to link the meaning of L2-words through
the corresponding surface form of L1 - and instead
devote his energy to other, more superficial or abstract
cues of the L2-material. This would be typical of a
cognitively more mature individual, who tends to apply
the most parsimonious yet efficient processing strategies
in such performance.

Our processing distinction gains further momentum if
it is fitted into a general framework of hemispheric
functioning. As mentioned before, the left hemisphere
seems to be specialized in sequential, analytic processes,
while the right tends to excel on simultaneous, holistic
tasks. Although it is easy to overdichotomize this
difference, as is often done (cf. McKeever's (1981) term
"dichotomania"), hemispheric functional similarities
being much more pronounced than corresponding differences,
the distinction has some genuine appeal, especially at
the perceptual level (Corballis, 1983).

There are two factors of overt relevance here, both
of which may have contributed to the development of our
language-specific processing patterns. On the one hand,
the sequential character of auditory input in general
may predispose such stimuli to left-hemisphere processing,
while the more simultaneous impact of visual input appears
to be relatively more compatible with right-hemisphere
abilities. This idea accords both with the hypothesized
superior pattern recognition ability of the right hemisphere (e.g. Bryden, 1960; Levy et al., 1972), the
linguistic relevance of which has been demonstrated for
both visual and tactile (braille) reading (e.g. Bryden &
Allard, 1976; Harris, 1980), and with the prevailing
notion from clinical research that deficient serial

processing, which is considered as one of the main
causes behind language impairment in aphasics, is
typically incurred through left-hemisphere damage (e.g.
Ellegård, 1982). On the other hand, and perhaps more
importantly, analysis of meaning is viewed as an
analytically-based function, and as such it is associated
primarily with the left hemisphere. Several semantic
interference tests have indicated that this hemisphere
processes meaning more readily than the right (e.g.
Cohen & Martin, 1975; Vaid & Lambert, 1979).

In the light of the evidence invoked above, then, the
most reasonable explanation of the present lateralization
pattern L1>L2 seems to be that the native and the foreign
language called upon different processing strategies,
which in their turn made different demands on the
respective characteristic perceptuocognitive abilities
of the cerebral hemispheres. Though there inevitably
exist other circumstantial factors influencing interlingual lateralization patterns, this model of differential
levels of processing - i.e. structural versus semantic -
appears to account for most of the recorded divergence
between the Swedish and English experimental results.[33]
What remains a problem, however, is that the visual
test, seemingly in conflict with our theory, consistently
gave higher LIs than the auditory, but as this phenomenon
probably has an artifactual cause, it will be left in
abeyance until we discuss the effect of experiment (LIs)
below.

Intergroup relations: If we turn to our next significant
effect in the experimental data - age/English proficiency
level (LIs) - a similar explanation applies. As we remember,

---

33. To explain the recorded language difference in terms
of differential cognitive modes à la Bogen (1969) - i.e.
propositional versus appositional processing - is not
realistic here. Such effects possibly occur between languages
that show marked structural discrepancies only, for example
Hopi and English (Rogers et al., 1977), and not between
similar ones like Swedish and English (cf. pp. 23-24).

the extent of inferred left-hemisphere lateralization
decreased with increasing level of age/proficiency so
that the least proficient Group A evinced the strongest
cerebral asymmetry and the most proficient Group C the
weakest, with the intermediate Group B falling in-
between.[34] This trend (A>B>C) deviates, however, from

34. At first sight, it is tempting to associate this
diminishing laterality effect with the improvement of
overall performance across age/English proficiency level
(cf. age/English proficiency level - raw scores). As
demonstrated before, the LIs decreased significantly
(in three cases out of four) when the number of identified
words increased (see notes 19 and 28), a correlation which
suggests that the laterality effect may have been conditioned to some extent by subjects' ability to perform
the test tasks. However, this interpretation is not
pressing, and in fact not even very likely. To claim that
our seemingly reciprocal parameters were interdependent
and that the decreasing laterality effect was an artifact
of this relation, arguably requires a ceiling effect in
the raw scores. This would obtain if so easy a task was
administered that subjects were able to identify all or
almost all the words presented to one or both ears/visual
fields, resulting in the relative differences between
the sides, which underlie the LI-computations, becoming
inaccurately low. Since there was no indication that
any ceiling effect occurred, however (cf. the combined
achieved score/total score mean ratio in each subject
group (in Table 7): Group A = 28/60, Group B = 34/60,
Group C = 39/60), it seems more plausible to view
overall performance and laterality as mutually independent,
but still originating from the same source. This source
is of course the age/English proficiency factor (perhaps
in interaction with some other factor(s)), the rising
value of which would thus be largely responsible for the
two demonstrated, apparently separate but coincidental
developments - i.e. the increase in word-identification
ability and the decrease in laterality. This also means,
reasonably, that the soundness of the laterality effect

that of the majority of previous studies, which rather
advocate an approximately constant degree of left-
hemisphere dominance, irrespective of degree of proficiency in L2 (see p. 21 ff.). To resolve this discord,
it is apparently necessary to go more deeply into the
test data again.

Starting with the previous studies, they are based on
a variety of experimental methods, implicating both
auditory and visual paradigms, as well as electrocortical
measures (see Genesee, 1982). The most immediate question
that arises is whether these differences of procedure in
any way correlate with particular types or tendencies of
laterality. Contrary to expectations, however, no obvious
interactions between hemispheric patterns and method or
modality emerged when we re-analyzed the results of these
tests a posteriori, nor were there any notable correlations
with type of L2-acquisition or language. This does not
mean that such effects were necessarily lacking, but
rather that they were not measurable in the heterogeneous
state of the data (cf. pp. 22-23). Consequently, neither
support nor any elucidating explanations of our declining
trend A>B>C is attainable by narrowing down the previous
material in this way. However, if we draw upon the
effects from our own statistical calculations, it is
possible to formulate a viable solution in terms of
deep and superficial processing, thus on the same lines
as in the foregoing discussion.

We must however first clarify the inherent potential
of the term age/English proficiency. Literally, it
encompasses two factors only, viz. the biological age
of subjects and their estimated proficiency in English.
But presumably there are two more factors. On the one
hand, subjects' intellectual ability seems to be correlated
with this dual concept, at least as suggested by the brief

---

need not be questioned on the basis of between-subject
variations in experienced task-difficulty or overall
performance, although such variations may well be used
to explain the different processes and strategies underlying it.

investigation of the relation between school marks and
educational level reported earlier (pp. 34-35). This
would be an effect of the progressively working student
drop-out factor, the value of which tends to increase
when the educational level is augmented. On the other
hand, our statistics indicate that native-language
proficiency also improves with a boosted age/English
proficiency level. As the number of identified English
words increased with rising L2-proficiency, there was a
concomitant, but less pronounced increment of identified
Swedish words (language x age/English proficiency level -
raw scores). This development of raw scores is of course
natural, since it constitutes a product of the continuously
maturing cognitive functions in young individuals in
general, whether bilinguals or monolinguals. Since there
was no interaction in the LI-data, however, these con-
verging proficiency trends apparently did not affect the
interlingual relation of lateralization over the different
subject groups.

We may base our argument on the recorded effect of
experiment x age/English proficiency level (raw scores).
This interaction implies that Group A performed better
on the auditory task than on the visual, whereas Group C
showed an opposite pattern, with superior achievement
on the visual task. Group B was midway between these two,
with about equal performance in both modalities. Inasmuch
as this trend was present in both languages, the crucial
factors behind it do not seem to concern so much the
languages per se as the different perceptuocognitive
approaches that subjects applied in carrying out the
test tasks.

Our demonstrated interaction is a logical outcome of
the differential conditions of cognitive maturity and
verbal experience that affect subjects. These conditions
implicate the previously identified components of the
concept age/English proficiency. First, the advance of
age from Group A to Group C suggests that there is a
corresponding (though not parallel) increase of cerebral
maturation and consequently also of cognitive ability -
the older the subject, the more flexible and abstraction-

prone his mental capacity.

Second, the increasing level of education and thus proficiency (in both languages) imports that there is an analogous trend in the amount of reading experience exhibited by the test population. While Group A still seem to be only moderately practised in visual language activity (=reading), the amount of exposure to this modality almost inevitably increases at the relative expense of the auditory domain, when the educational/ proficiency level is enhanced. In other words, Group B subjects, and more particularly Group C subjects, may be expected to be more experienced readers (and writers) than those of Group A as a result of their longer training (cf. Macnamara, 1970). Hence, they are presumed to be more at ease in the visual modality than the less educated subjects of Group A.

If the above between-group differences are connected with Craik & Lockhart's (1972) deep-superficial processing distinction, we may parallel the preceding discussion of interlingual differences. Our speculation is that along the continuum of age/English proficiency, there was a gradual shift of processing strategies, so that the youngest and least proficient subjects used a relatively deep or semantic approach to verbal stimuli, and the oldest and most proficient a somewhat more superficial, but presumably more efficient mode of analysis.[35] On previous grounds (p. 79 ff.), this hypothesis is supported by the demonstrated performance dissociation over modality. The auditory preponderance in Group A argues for a higher degree of semantic processing in the lower range of age/proficiency, and conversely, the visual advantage in Group C bespeaks a focus on cursory pattern- or code-based strategies in the older and more proficient subjects, while Group B again assumes a neutral position in-between these.

---

35. A similar structural-semantic processing distinction has been noted between early and late bilinguals, where the former group showed relatively more semantic, or less structural, processing than the latter (Genesee et al., 1978).

This view also agrees with the putative effect of
intellectual ability. The "smarter" subjects in the
higher range of age/proficiency presumably tried to
disregard the semantic aspects of the stimuli, since no
comprehension was required in the tests, and instead
concentrated on those features which appeared most
important for optimal perception, short-term retention,
and graphic reproduction, for example visual and
auditory surface codes. (The fact that they were more
successful with the visual material would mirror their
relatively greater visual training.) The younger and less
mature subjects, on the other hand, would be cognitively
more limited and also more dependent on the semantic
strategies of the native language, and therefore not
capable of circumventing the "irrelevant" meaning
analysis to the same extent. Though their mode of processing probably is a more accurate reflection of natural
language use, it seems unnecessarily clumsy and redundant
in our experimental context.

We may thus explain the regressive trend of lateralization over age/English proficiency level in terms of the
same strategy model as before. While the basic, genetic
component of hemispheric language specialization is seen
as remaining roughly stable in all types of subjects
(cf. the average of previous studies, which advocates
A=B=C), the demonstrated between-group differences of
laterality here seem to be due to the hypothesized shift
in modes of processing, which in its turn seems to derive
from a combination of subject differences in linguistic
and cognitive status and experienced task difficulty.
As propounded in the interlingual section, deep or
semantic processing of words involves primarily left-
hemisphere activity (analytic), while superficial or
pattern-based processing appears to utilize the hemispheres more equally (analytic + synthetic). The lateralization patterns would then alter gradually from a strong
left-hemisphere bias in Group A, through the intermediate
stage of Group B, to a more moderate advantage for this
side in Group C as the levels of cognitive maturity and
language proficiency are augmented. Though these factors

cannot be isolated from other circumstantial variables,
they seem to be essential for how the bilingual approaches
a verbal task. Consequently, the increasing flexibility
of cognitive and linguistic repertoire over subjects may
be seen as reflected in the pattern of declining laterality,
A>B>C.

Interexperimental relations: Our last significant
effect of laterality concerns the method. The recorded
experiment (LIs) mirrors the differential results from the
auditory and visual tests, where the former constantly
yielded lower LI-values than the latter. There seem to
be two different, but interconnected explanations of this
outcome, both of which relate to the type of experimental
procedure employed.

If we start with what seems to be the purely artifactual
part of the problem, it pertains to the distinction of
auditory and visual modality. Prima facie, one would expect
the visual test to exhibit slightly lower laterality than
the auditory one, inasmuch as visual activity previously
has been associated with weaker left-right differences
than corresponding auditory processes. The present effect
(visual > auditory) would thus contradict this relation.
But if our finding is examined more in detail, it becomes
apparent that we are faced with another aspect of the
modality distinction here. What has been discussed on the
preceding pages is a diachronically evolved effect of
individual language experience and development as manifested
in different neuropsychological processing patterns. Now,
on the other hand, we are dealing with a momentary modality
effect, which presumably is conditioned by distinct test
methods rather than by type of language background or
cognitive status.

One of the most obvious differences between the
auditory and visual tests is the perceptual processes
they presuppose. While the auditory method appears
relatively straightforward, the visual technique brings
about certain inherent difficulties, two of which are of
specific relevance here. The first has already been
mentioned in the introductory section of the visual test,

viz. a left-to-right reading scan habit, which tends to
favour the right visual field to some extent in word-
identification tasks. This tendency is usually taken to
be caused by an implicit "post-exposure process", i.e.
the concert (right-field) or disconcert (left-field) of a
dominant eye-movement towards the beginning of any
presented verbal stimuli and a subordinate movement
from left to right across this material (Harcum & Finkel,
1963). The second factor refers to a greater perceptual
sensitivity near fixation as compared to more peripheral
positions in the visual field - Overton & Wiener (1966)
have suggested that since the beginning of a word is more
essential to the identification of it than the end, the
fact that the initial letters of right-field words fall
close to fixation, whereas the initial letters of left-
field words fall further out in the periphery, may entail
inadequate right-field advantages in tachistoscopic tests
and similar paradigms. Thus, although these perceptual
factors do not concern cerebral processing per se, they
may boost the visually recorded left-lateralization
effects in relation to the auditory findings. In this
manner, methodological artifacts may account for the
differential results of our experiments.[36]

However, the answer is not as simple as a pure additive
relationship. Though artifactual influence probably
contributes a certain portion of the right visual field
advantage, we do not achieve a balanced, clear-cut
relation between the auditory and visual findings by
merely noting the average difference between the laterality
indices from the two modalities. The reason for this is
that there was only a weak correlation between them (r =

---

36. To argue that the purported artifacts from the visual
test procedure account for the whole left-lateralization
effect is, however, not realistic, since there were
also subjects who evinced an advantage for the left
visual field (seven in the Swedish test and 11 in the
English). According to such a theory, no inverted patterns
would be possible as long as the target scripts are read
from left to right.

.17, p=.19), which indicates that the parallelism over experiment in fact was rather low (cf. Bryden, 1965; 1982, who experienced a similar pattern). Contrary to expectations, then, the visual and auditory lateralization patterns in the individual subjects do not seem to be related to any great extent. The lack of correlation rather implies that our test methods gauged partially distinct effects of the basic word-identification task, not necessarily in terms of modality differences, but in terms of more general perceptuocognitive functions. If this is so, we must try to identify the possible sources of these effects in the experimental procedures, and tentatively relate them to the test findings.

When scrutinizing our investigation methods, we find that they tap somewhat different cognitive skills in the individual. In the auditory test, a block of stimuli was presented in about seven seconds (3 x 2 words with intervals of 2.0 seconds). Such a presentational technique puts high demands on the ability to memorize many items in a short period of time. In the visual test, on the other hand, the crucial process appears to be stimulus perception - each word was exposed for 100 milliseconds only, whereas the total duration of a block of words was almost 20 seconds (6 x 1 word with intervals of 3.8 seconds). The auditory task accordingly appears as a memory trial essentially, with no perceptual problems per se (both words of a pair were heard clearly), while the visual task conversely seems to be more of a test of perceptual ability, with less pronounced memorizing problems. A similar characterization of these tasks may be derived from sundry spontaneous remarks by the subjects after they had completed the test series: "I heard the words, but I still couldn't remember them afterwards", and "it was hard to see the words, because they disappeared so quickly".

As we know by now, lateralization of receptive functions may be defined as a biased relationship between the cerebral hemispheres in terms of, among other things, the ability to perceive and store verbal material. In other words, this concept involves two important aspects

of linguistic processing – perception (transmission of
information over the afferent pathways from sensory organ
to cerebral receiving area) and memory (intracerebral
storage). If we consider the hypothesis that the present
test methods emphasize these functions differently, we
seem to have a clue as to why our results failed to
correlate over experiment.

First, it is possible that the differential neuroanatomical arrangements of the auditory and visual input
systems have influenced the data. While, somewhat
simplistically put, the connections of the visual
system are crossed so that each visual half-field
projects information directly to the opposite hemisphere (see Figure 5), the auditory system displays a
more complex structure, with only a partial decussation
of the pathways between the ears and the hemispheres
(see Figure 1). Exclusive crossing of auditory input à la
the visual mode is thought to obtain in cases of competitive stimulation of the left and right ears (Kimura,
1961b), but since there exist ipsilateral connections
as well, we cannot be sure that these are shut out
completely during dichotic testing. If these pathways
do contribute in any way to information mediation here,
it appears to be in terms of covert cueing between ear
and hemisphere on each side, a phenomenon which,
probabilistically speaking, would diminish the differences
of recorded hit-rate between the ears. The consequence of
this would be that the inferred lateralization patterns
become less asymmetrical overall on artificial grounds.
Thus, with the possible effect of differential input
channelling, a certain divergence between the auditory
and visual results may have evolved, which, amplified by
the different perceptual demands over the tasks, may be
associated with the demonstrated low correlation in the
data. If this effect is real, however, it will unfortunately
also detract from the reliability of the dichotic method
in general.

A second argument is the different mnemonic techniques
which appear to have been used. After the test sessions,
quite a few subjects admitted that, despite instructions

to the contrary, they had consciously applied a pairing-
strategy in the auditory test to be able to remember
better. Words presented simultaneously to the left and
right ears were fused into "chunks", e.g. dog and bed
turned into dog-bed, in order to reduce the number of
items to be held in short-term memory (cf. Miller, 1956).
With this strategy, potential differences between the
ears/hemispheres become harder to detect, inasmuch as the
words are continuously linked together in left-right
pairs, so that if you fail to retain, say, a left-ear
word, the right is likely to drop out as well.

In the visual test, a similar mnemonic technique was
used occasionally, but it seems to have been much less
frequent, presumably because the successive mode of
stimulus presentation did not invite such a strategy to
the same extent. In those cases where stimulus-pairing
nevertheless was applied, it still did not affect the
left-right-side relationship as in the auditory test –
the visual words were randomly presented over the left
and right visual fields, with the probability being
about equal that a word from one field would be coupled
with another word from the same field as with one from
the opposite field.

Hence, a combination of high demands on efficient
memorizing and a pairwise presentational procedure in
the auditory test seem to have led to a synthetic approach
to the task, which is not paralleled in the visual test
as it stands. This associative technique may have deflated
our subjects' degree of lateralization in the auditory
test somewhat, and thereby contributed to the lack of
correlation between the auditory and visual findings.

Taken as a whole, then, several plausible explanations
for the differential results from our two experiments
may be arrived at. While the numerical preponderance of
the visual LIs seems to be due primarily to perceptual
artifacts of screen-viewing, the low correlation between
the two tests would be accounted for by the composite
effect of distinct neuroanatomical structures employed,
different presentational techniques, and a differential
emphasis of perception versus memory processing. Though

the above discussion is rather speculative, as is almost
inevitable in this context, it has hopefully conveyed an
insight into how complex is the issue of neuropsychological experimentation, and the theories put forward
here should therefore only be taken as one possible
solution of the problem. (Cf. also Bryden, 1965; Blumstein
et al., 1975; Colbourn, 1978.)

Sex and familial handedness: Finally, some comment on
the results of sex and familial handedness is justified.
As we remember, neither of these variables generated any
significant differences of lateralization, but rather
indicated a roughly stable pattern of left-hemisphere
dominance for both males and females, and subjects with
and without familial left-handers respectively. How do
these findings relate to our previously explicated model
of language organization?

Starting with subject sex, the approximate equivalence
of hemispheric specialization between males and females
suggested by the majority of earlier studies (pp. 17-18)
is confirmed by the present experiments. Interestingly
enough, the occasionally demonstrated bias towards less
lateralization in females obtained here as well, with a
marginally lower mean LI for this category (9.4 vs. 9.8;
cf. Kimura, 1983). Some researchers have associated this
tendency with certain biological differences over sex –
for example differential pubescent ages (e.g. Waber, 1977)
– or with differences of social background or cognitive
strategy application (e.g. Fairweather, 1976; Bryden,
1980). However, since the evidence underlying these
proposals is limited and our own trend was far from
being significant (p=.82), we will not press the matter
any further here.

But if we proceed to the raw data, we find a significant
interaction involving sex, viz. language x sex (raw scores).
This effect represents a trend for females to exhibit a
greater interlingual difference of recalled stimulus
words than males, where the operative factor seems to be
an unexpectedly low number of reported English words by
females (Swedish: males = 36.3, females = 35.4; English:

males = 33.2, females = 30.5). As also the overall
incidence of recalled words was lower for females (32.9
vs. 34.7), it is tempting to connect this effect with
the tendency of lower laterality in females just hinted
at, but as we know, this requires stronger evidence.

What looks suspicious here, however, is the fact that
most of the recorded divergence between the sexes
originates from Group B. This observation rather suggests
an explanation in terms of a sampling artifact, where the
females of this group accidentally may have been slightly
less proficient in English (and Swedish) than the corresponding males. If, in a procrustean manner, we deduct
the hypothetically irrelevant contribution of Group B
as measured by the magnitudes of the differences in the
two other groups, the present interaction is, if not
eliminated, greatly diminished (cf. Table 7).

For familial handedness, the expected tendency of
weaker hemispheric asymmetry in subjects with left-handed
parents or siblings was not found. Quite the reverse,
this group evinced on the average a somewhat stronger
left-lateralization than did the remaining "ordinary"
subjects (cf. Warrington & Pratt, 1973), but since the
groups were uneven concerning number of subjects and the
LI-data varied a great deal in both of them (cf. the low
F-values in the respective tests), we must not draw any
rash conclusions on the basis of this opposition. What
we need to do, however, is to try to find a reasonable
explanation as to why the present data did not attune
to previous research findings (p. 17).

Theoretically, there are two alternative solutions to
the problem. On the one hand, it is possible that there
is no effect of familial handedness on cerebral
lateralization of language, but that subjects' own
hand preference is what counts only. Findings from
earlier studies would then have been misinterpreted or
based on artifacts, which in itself is not all-out
inconceivable. In this case, our pattern of equal
lateralization over familial handedness would reflect
the true state of cerebral organization.

On the other hand, and more realistically, the present

experiments may somehow have failed to detect the proper
effect of familial handedness as indicated by previous
research. If this is true, the default may be caused
either by the target effect being obscured by other,
more influential subject characteristics or by inexpedient
probe techniques, or both. One plausible source of error
is, for example, the categorization of subjects into such
having and not having sinistrality in the family. As this
concept ideally denotes a hereditary effect based on
genetic predispositions, and not any fortuitous influence
of the environment, we realized a posteriori that our
criteria of familial left-handedness might have been too
superficial for an apt distinction – while our requirements
stated the presence of only one left-handed family member,
Hardyck (1977) has claimed that there should be three
left-handed family members spanning at least two genera-
tions to ensure a reliable effect and to avoid misclassi-
fications of this factor.

Another dubious point is the low number of observations.
With only 12 instances of familial sinistrality recorded,
and the remaining 48 subjects functioning as controls,
the performed statistical comparison undeniably looks a
bit halting. Furthermore, if some of these 12 cases are
wrongly classified, it is no surprise if we should end
up amiss of the expected outcome.

Despite the above shortcomings, however, we may
establish the probable relation between sex and familial
handedness, and cerebral lateralization. Since, theoretically,
both these factors pertain to the congenital nature of the
individual and his brain, they should be related primarily
to the base-level component of language organization –
"the deeper, neurophysiological processes of verbal storage
and function" (p. 78). Accordingly, inasmuch as sex and
familial handedness do not covary with other, developmental factors, we need not be detained by considerations
of possibly differential processing patterns in terms of
semantic or structural analysis as influencing our test
findings, but the data should rather speak to more
fundamental strata of the brain. We can thus establish
that sex does not seem to affect the hemispheric status

of language in our subjects, though certain maturational
and sociopsychological conditions interacting with sex
occasionally might have given us that impression in
earlier studies. It rather implies that the notion of a
stable, genetically-derived preponderance for left-
hemisphere processing of language is valid also over sex.

Familial handedness, on the other hand, being a form
of "secondary" handedness as regards cerebral organization,
presumably modifies the effect of subjects' primary hand
preference on lateralization. Theoretically, if there is
only dextrality in the family, this would reinforce
dextral subjects' typical left-lateralization, but if
there is sinistrality to various extents, the left-
dominance would diminish somewhat. This may be said,
since primary handedness has been shown to bear a strong,
and familial handedness a weak, relation to hemispheric
asymmetry of language along these lines (cf. Bryden, 1982;
Corballis, 1983). We will thus argue that despite the fact
that we were not able to demonstrate any effect of the
familial factor in our subjects, there is probably a
delicate influence of this factor in most bilinguals.
As such, it seems to act as a subfactor to the general
handedness parameter, along which, in contrast to sex,
the basic component of language lateralization does vary
somewhat. Due to the purported delicacy of familial
handedness influence, it may be measured to different
degrees in different investigations, depending on how
strong the effects from other constituents of the test
situation are. In our experiments, this factor was, if
not lacking or misinterpreted, most likely absorbed by
other individual characteristics or methodological
properties.

Summary: If we try to sum up our chapter on bilingual
lateralization, then, the following points may be made.
(1) The internal lexical representation, whether
Swedish or English, seems to be lateralized to the left
cerebral hemisphere in the majority of our dextral
Swedish-English subsidiary bilinguals. In conformity
with earlier research, this bias would be the result of

a genetic predisposition of the brain in favour of the left hemisphere, a specialization which apparently also has a measurable anatomical base.

(2) The Swedish lexical system appears to be somewhat more left-lateralized than the English. Specifically, this difference is thought to be generated by different processing strategies for the native and the foreign language, which tend to draw on the characteristic perceptuocognitive abilities of the two hemispheres slightly differently. Though this might smack of neo-Whorfianism, the effect is seen as caused primarily by differential language acquisition histories.

(3) The recorded degree of left-hemisphere dominance decreased with increasing age/English proficiency level. This trend presumably stems from differential processing strategies as well, engendered by differences of cognitive and linguistic experience across the three test groups.

(4) The visual test indicated stronger left-lateralization than the auditory test. Since a theory in terms of separate auditory and visual lexical systems seems unlikely, this divergence is probably best explained as an at least partially artificial effect of the distinct investigation methods applied.

(5) Males and females appear to be equal regarding the extent of left-hemisphere dominance.

(6) No difference of left-lateralization between subjects with and without familial traits of sinistrality was recorded. It is probable, however, that the appropriate effect from this factor was obscured by other, more prominent subject characteristics or imperfect test conditions.

III. Interdependence

We will now put the localizational perspective on the brain aside for a while and instead focus on more functional aspects of language organization. As already mentioned in Chapter I, our objective here is to chart the functional relation between the languages in bilinguals by investigating the degree of interdependence that may exist between them. In particular, we are interested in the neuropsychological organization of the morphological subsystems and what type of factors are influential in this context. For instance, one may ask whether there is interdependence within this field at all – some scholars seem to be rather sceptical about this (see the discussion of morphological interference in Weinreich, 1953) – and if there is, whether it is possible to demonstrate it experimentally in receptive verbal performance. One way to approach this issue – and the method we will use – is to measure potential interference in bilinguals processing morphological material, and then test whatever findings we achieve against different models of functional language organization.

First, however, is an eclectic review of previous functional studies on the bilingual brain in general. In this, we will try to assess the current state of affairs by marshalling some of the evidence that has been adduced for and against language independence and interdependence within different linguistic strata. Parallelling the arrangement of the background material in Chapter II, this survey will be divided into <u>clinical</u> and <u>experimental studies</u>. The former type thus involves primarily pathological data from bilingual aphasic patients, while the latter, which is the main source of information here, refers to a variety of psycholinguistic investigations of the non-damaged bilingual brain. Thereafter, on the basis of the findings from these studies, we will attempt to identify and evaluate different factors behind or concurrent with the bilingual state, which might affect the functional relation between the languages.

1. Clinical studies

From a clinical viewpoint, the issue of independence
versus interdependence of the languages of bilinguals
has often been discussed in terms of the tangible notions
of separate versus shared language centers. However, since
these terms are somewhat unsatisfactory in relation to
the current state of research, no explicit centers of
language being reckoned with (e.g. Ellegård, 1982),
we prefer to use the more functionally-oriented terms
separate versus shared language systems here. Whatever
denomination used, the distinction is employed to
differentiate two hypothesized modes of linguistic
organization in the brain - either two separate systems
for the processing and storage of the languages, one
for each of them (independence), or a common system for
both (interdependence). Though a strict dichotomy of
these concepts may be unrealistic, as will be indicated
later on, the application of it has been of considerable
heuristic value in identifying key problems within the
field of brain-language research.

There is a great deal of data from patterns of impairment and recovery in bilingual aphasics which has been
brought to bear on the topic of separate versus shared
language systems. In the corresponding section of Chapter
II, we discussed this matter in terms of different
calculations of the incidence of (primarily expressive)
language dissociation - i.e. unparallel derangement or
restitution of the languages - observed in brain-damaged
bilinguals. From that review, it appeared that whereas
selected case studies indicated differential symptoms in
50-60% of the instances, random case studies, which
probably reflect the true frequency more accurately,
showed an incidence around 10% only (see p. 9). If, as
suggested by Lambert & Fillenbaum (1959) and others,
language dissociation is taken as evidence for separate
language systems, where the damage has affected one
language only, and lack of dissociation conversely as
evidence for common systems, where parallel symptoms
have obtained, these scores indicate that the existence

of separate language systems is relatively scarce, and
that most bilinguals rather ought to be viewed as having
essentially shared systems. A reservation must be made
here, however, as to the proportion of aphasics who
seem to exhibit separation. It is possible that some of
the patients that properly belong to this category have
been wrongly classified as sharers, because their language
systems, despite mutual separation, have been equally
affected by the cerebral damage.

Moreover, the aphasiological data have indicated that
there exist differential symptoms not only between the
languages as wholes, but also between the expressive and
receptive modalities, and between the different linguistic
strata. For example, Albert & Obler (1978) reported that
in those cases where language dissociation obtained in
their bilingual aphasics, it often affected the relation
between production and comprehension abilities. While one
language suffered severe impairment in speech and writing,
the other would remain altogether undisturbed, or while
one language was totally lost, the other would be
retained in comprehension.

Similarly, unparallel disturbances have been recorded
over the corresponding phonological, morphological,
lexical, and syntactical subsystems of the bilinguals'
languages. In Albert & Obler's (1978) investigation,
there are a variety of instances of this phenomenon.
Most of the selective symptoms have been observed at the
lexical level - some 20 cases indicate that the language-
specific lexical representations are differentially
impaired by the cerebral damage incurred, since word-
finding or word-reading abilities are hampered to
different extents over the languages (selective alexia
or anomia). At the other levels, differentiation seems
to be less frequent. 11 cases of unparallel derangement
of the patients' syntactical or morphological abilities
are reported, where word-order properties or other
grammatical features are lacking or inappropriately used
in one or the other language (selective agrammatism or
dysarthria). Differential phonological disturbances,
finally, have been observed in two cases only, where

sound production or accent deficits differed across the
languages.

In spite of the fact that the above evidence consists
of a great deal of fragmentary material and subjective
evaluation of different aphasic symptoms, it may be used
to make some tentative inferences about the organization
of the various linguistic subsystems in bilinguals. First,
the relatively high incidence of aphasic dissociation
between the expressive and receptive modalities implies
that these systems are independent to some extent as
regards their neuropsychological representation. Since
this notion tallies quite well with the previously
presented lateralization evidence, language production
being more acutely lateralized towards the left hemisphere than comprehension, this seems to be a reasonable
conclusion. Second, the unequal distribution across the
range of linguistic strata suggests that there may exist
differences of organization between these systems too.
The data reviewed seem to indicate that in the bilingual
brain, the lexical systems are mutually more independent
than the morphological and syntactical ones respectively,
while the phonological systems are largely interdependent.
It should be borne in mind, however, that the evidence
underlying this proposal is very limited, and may be
influenced by a bias of interest towards lexical
disturbances. Therefore, no conclusions should be drawn
on the basis of our clinical material only (see further
Section 2).

Finally, a few words may also be said about interlingual interference. In a clinical context, this concept
is used to refer to sundry instances of language mixing
in bilingual aphasics, which did not occur premorbidly,
but arose as a consequence of damage to the brain. For
example, while using one language, a patient may insert
words or phrases from another language, employ foreign
syntax patterns, or even transfer inflections between
languages. The attention allocated to this type of interference problem seems to be rather scanty, though, and
this is probably because the syndrome in itself is fairly
rare. Paradis (1977) mentioned only 17 instances of post-

traumatic interference in his review of 138 aphasic
cases (12%), and similarly Albert & Obler (1978) noted
16 out of 108 cases in their study (15%). Further, if
we take into account that these figures derive from
selected case studies (see p. 9), it seems likely that
the true incidence is even lower.

It is questionable, however, whether interference
data from aphasics can open up any vistas to the issue
of linguistic independence versus interdependence in
the brain. Whereas the cerebral insult obviously has
disturbed or destroyed the "mechanism" that is
responsible for selective channelling of the languages,
whether this is a simple on-off switch mechanism or a
flexible, continuously working monitor system (see p.
110), we do not know what type of organization it subserved premorbidly. Logically, this is because some
form of psychological control function must be postulated
in both the separated and integrated version of language
organization, and thus, although interference in healthy
bilinguals is thought to occur between shared systems
only, it may obtain under both conditions in aphasics
when this function is disturbed.

2. Experimental studies

The main body of data on the functional organization
of language in bilinguals stems from experimental studies.
In contrast to the rather limited clinical discipline,
this domain abounds with intriguing approaches as to the
type of relation that exists between the languages in
the brain, both in terms of expressive and receptive
processing. Focusing on healthy bilinguals, the methods
of investigation range from pure field studies of every-
day verbal performance to various sophisticated test
settings where different models of language organization
are experimentally evaluated. As will become apparent
below, the findings from these inquiries have enabled
researchers to study more closely the different factors

that seem to condition the functional state of bilingualism.

In psycholinguistic research, the notions of separate versus shared language systems have commonly been referred to in terms of <u>coordinate</u> versus <u>compound systems</u> (e.g. Weinreich, 1953; Ervin & Osgood, 1954).[37] Though there might exist subtle differences of meaning between these pairs of terms occasionally, they seem to correspond quite closely and we will therefore use them inter- changeable in the following.

A large portion of the experimental research carried out has centered around the coordinate–compound distinc- tion of language organization. In particular, much work has been devoted to modulate the originally strictly dichotomous character of this theoretical construct, which, it was claimed, did not correspond to a flexible neuropsychological reality (e.g. Diller, 1974). A number of modifications of it has thus led to a position where today few would assert that bilinguals are <u>either</u> coordinate or compound. Rather, the prevalent idea appears to be to regard them as lying somewhere along a continuum between these poles, where the underlying correlates of language exhibit both sharing and separation in different proportions in different individuals (e.g. Riegel, 1968; Diller, 1974). The more specific position for each bilingual on this scale is seen as a function of, for example, context of language acquisition, type of language, or personal characteristics (see Section 3).

The picture is, as implied before, further complicated by what seems to be an uneven distribution of compound and coordinate organization over the expressive and receptive modalities, and over the different linguistic strata. Several experimental studies have shown that while the productive systems of the bilinguals' languages

---

37. In addition, Weinreich (1953) reckoned with a third type of interlingual relation, namely <u>subordinate organi- zation</u>. This would be a subtype of compound organization (and is as such mostly fused with this), where L2 is seen as mediated through – and hence dependent on – L1 by means of translation processes.

are independent of each other to a considerable degree,
the comprehension systems tend to be more interdependent
(e.g. Caramazza et al., 1973; Ervin, 1961; Kolers, 1966).

Likewise, the phonological, morphological, lexical,
and syntactical systems have been ascribed different
extents of language separation or sharing in the brain
on the basis of various experimental evidence. Probably
because lexical items are relatively easy to define and
test, the relation between the lexical representations
have received most attention. Four main types of investigation seem to have been applied here, viz.
association tests (e.g. Kolers, 1963; Gekoski, 1970),
list recall tasks (e.g. Lambert et al., 1958; Kintsch,
1977), lexicosemantic tests (e.g. Jacobovits & Lambert,
1961; Hamers & Lambert, 1972), and analyses of general
lexical interference (e.g. Weinreich, 1953; Vildomec,
1963). This multifaceted approach has no doubt resolved
many minor problems of bilingual lexical organization, but
it still has not enabled us to draw any definite conclusion
as to whether the language-specific systems are primarily
coordinate or compound. The reason for this is that the
different forms of lexical connection that have been
demonstrated within and across languages have split
scholars into two parties - one which advocates the
independence position (e.g. Kolers, 1963; Tulving &
Colotla, 1970; Scarborough et al., 1984) and another
which rather supports the notion of interdependence (e.g.
Rose et al., 1975; McCormack, 1977; Nas, 1983). A
reasonable escape from this impasse is perhaps to view
the lexical systems as both coordinate and compound,
depending in part upon the perspective we assume when
observing or testing them (cf. Obler, 1981).

If we proceed to the syntactical domain, the amount
of information pertaining to the organization of these
systems is not quite as rich. Two methods of inquiry
may be mentioned, viz. sentence processing tasks (e.g.
Doob, 1957; MacKay & Bowman, 1969) and analyses of
general syntactical interference (e.g. Duškova, 1969;
LoCoco, 1975). Most of the data from these studies
indicate that there is a certain degree of inter-

dependence between the bilinguals' syntactical systems, since both syntactical facilitation and inhibition across language have been shown to obtain on several occasions. It is uncertain, however, whether this evidence is strong enough to justify a labelling of the organization as compound, especially since suggestions have also been made in the opposite direction (see for example Albert & Obler (1978), who proposed a coordinate state). It seems wise therefore to assume a neutral position regarding this question and view the syntactical systems as roughly intermediate on the compound-coordinate continuum.

At the morphological level, the picture is seemingly somewhat clearer. Although the evidence apparently is limited to a single source only, viz. analyses of general morphological interference (e.g. Vildomec, 1963; Duškova, 1969), there is a consensus of opinion claiming that the morphological systems in bilinguals are independent of each other to a great extent. This conclusion is based on the consistently low frequency of cross-language intrusions of free or bound morphemes that has been observed in different investigations of bilingual verbal production. A crucial lacuna here, however, is that little attention has been paid to receptive aspects of language processing (which we will try to remedy somewhat in the following). It is thus possible that this approach would come up with a different result, but in the current state of knowledge we must classify the morphological systems as essentially coordinate.

The organization at the phonological level, finally, has been probed primarily through auditory categorization tasks (e.g. Scholes, 1968; Anisfeld et al., 1969) and analyses of general phonological interference (e.g. Weinreich, 1953; Vildomec, 1963). These studies have suggested that the phonological systems are for the most part interdependent, since considerable interinfluence has been demonstrated in various groups of test subjects. This view becomes even more plausible if we take into account that the phonological level is thought to be the stronghold of interference in bilinguals, where "foreign accents" may persist in otherwise uncontaminated verbal

performance. Hence, in contrast to the morphological
level, the phonological systems seem to be principally
compound in the average bilingual.

The notion of a neuropsychological <u>switch mechanism</u>
has also been dealt with in experimental research. This
concept was originally proposed by neurologists who
sought a means of explaining the remarkable ability of
bilinguals to keep their languages apart (e.g. Poetzl,
1930; Goldstein, 1948). According to Penfield & Roberts
(1959), the switch would govern two functionally separate
language systems in the brain in such a way that when
one is on, the other must be off. Several experiments
have been carried out to investigate aspects of this
theory - for example, Macnamara & Kushnir (1971) measured
the time required to switch languages in production and
comprehension, Macnamara (1966) studied the effect of
language anticipation on switching facility, and Ervin-
Tripp (1968) attempted to determine what factors are
likely to trigger the switch.

The concept of a simple on-off switch mechanism has
met with a great deal of opposition, however, since it
does not account for the numerous instances of interlingual interference that has been shown to obtain in
bilinguals, nor for the existence of simultaneous translators (e.g. Albert & Obler, 1978). If one language
system is activated at a time only, there can hardly
occur any co-activity or influence from the system that
is shut off.

To resolve this problem, Obler & Albert (1978)
suggested an internal <u>monitor system</u> as responsible
for the unilingual channelling of verbal performance.
This system would never switch one language off entirely,
but would always be prepared to process both languages,
relying on certain probability computations from both
linguistic and extralinguistic factors. Consequently,
both parallel activity and cross-language influence would
be possible in this case. Thus, although it is hard to
assess its neuropsychological validity, the monitor
theory takes on more respectability than that of the
switch mechanism, as it is reconcilable with the different

occurrences of bilingual interference, as well as with
the instances of double language processing evinced by
simultaneous translators.

The contribution of the switch and monitor hypotheses
to the issue of coordinate versus compound language
organization is unclear, however. Although, on intuitive
grounds, they seem more compatible with a coordinate
state (cf. Penfield & Roberts, 1959), there must exist
some type of "control mechanism" in both types of
organization, since both coordinate and compound
bilinguals are able to keep their performance essentially
unilingual. As interference is thought to occur in compound
bilinguals only, it may be that this mechanism is less
efficient - or "leaky", to use Taylor's (1976a) term -
here, allowing cross-language influence to take place in
these individuals. In coordinate bilinguals, on the other
hand, a more stringent device would preside over the
channelling of language, where interference is always
precluded, theoretically speaking.

It is premature, however, to draw any conclusions from
this theorizing, since it rests on mere speculation, or
at the most, vague research findings. Studies of, for
example, switch latencies or factors triggering switching
(see above) cannot as yet be used to argue convincingly
for or against a certain type of language organization in
the brain.

3. Factors conditioning functional organization

From the preceding general review of studies on the
functional relation between the bilinguals' languages,
we will now go into particulars of this matter in terms
of the underlying causes of different types of interlingual organization. By fusing the data from the clinical
and experimental fields, we will attempt to identify and
evaluate some of the factors that may condition the
degree of language independence versus interdependence
in the brain. As before, the conspectus will include

three different types of presumably relevant material, viz.
individual-specific, language-acquisitional, and language-
specific factors. It deserves mentioning again, however,
that none of the factors put forward here are to be
regarded as independent explanations of the present
problem. Rather, although they are dealt with separately,
they should be viewed as single components of a complex
interaction of many different factors, on which the
pertinent type of language organization depends.

3.1. Individual-specific factors

In general, no explicit claims seem to have been made
concerning the potential influence of individual-specific
factors in the present context. On the contrary, most of
the pertinent studies have refrained from analyzing this
type of data, or even ignored its very existence (cf.
for example Kintsch & Kintsch, 1969; Taylor, 1971;
Neufeld, 1976). These shortcomings do however not mean
that such factors are necessarily irrelevant to language
interaction patterns in the brain. Instead, since we
know virtually nothing about the matter, some form of
examination is called for.

To achieve a rough evaluation of possibly relevant
individual-specific factors, we have re-analyzed the
data from Albert & Obler's (1978) review of 108 aphasic
cases over the variables of hand preference, sex, and
age. Despite the amount of information on personal
characteristics being meagre at times, such an approach
may at least give us a clue as to whether it is needful
to consider this type of data in discussions of language
independence-interdependence.

Hand preference: We know from the lateralization
evidence reported in Chapter II that handedness bears
a significant relation to hemispheric organization in
bilinguals. In particular, right-handers tend to exhibit
on the average a stronger lateralization of the language

systems to the left hemisphere than do left-handers (see
p. 16). One might thus wonder whether this factor also
affects the functional relationship between the languages
in any measurable way. For example, are right-handers
more likely to show interdependent, and left-handers
independent, language organization, is it perhaps the
other way round, or is there no difference at all between
them?

Unfortunately, there are only 22 cases in Albert &
Obler's (1978) study where the patients' handedness is
either explicitly stated or inferable. Of these, 13 refer
to right-handers and nine to left-handers. If the
aphasiological symptoms in these patients are examined,
we find that four right-handers and five left-handers
(of whom two were ambidextrals) evinced differential
impairment or restitution of their languages (31% and
56% respectively), whereas the remaining nine right-
handers and four left-handers showed parallel aphasic
syndromes (69% and 44% respectively). As unparallel
symptoms are thought to derive from a coordinate state
and parallel symptoms conversely from a compound state,
there is apparently a trend for left-handers to be more
coordinately organized in the brain than right-handers,
who rather seem to rely on primarily compound language
systems. The weight of this difference is of course
quite limited, since it stems from such a small number
of observations, but the pattern is nonetheless interesting.
As left-handers tend to display more equivocal, not to say
conflicting, patterns of lateralization than right-
handers (e.g. Zangwill, 1960), it is possible that this
heterogeneity is coupled with greater functional separation
between the languages. However, since the degree of
accuracy and generalizability in the present data is
hard to determine, we will not draw any conclusion
regarding the effect of handedness on interlingual
organization until further studies have been carried out.

Sex: Another possible factor in this context is subject
sex. As we remember, no major influence was attributed to
this variable concerning different types of lateralization

patterns in bilinguals. Is the same true for functional
language relations in such individuals, or is there a
selective sex effect dissociating males and females in
any way regarding this aspect of organization?

Returning to Albert & Obler's (1978) aphasiological
data, we find that there are 106 cases, involving 84
males and 22 females[38], which are relevant to this issue.
63 males and 14 females exhibited differential aphasic
symptoms over their languages (75% and 64% respectively),
while 21 males and eight females showed parallel
disturbances (25% and 36% respectively). These scores
may be interpreted as showing that males are on the
average slightly more coordinate (or less compound) than
females, since there was a higher incidence of unparallel
aphasic symptoms in this group.

Again, however, we are faced with reliability problems
in our observations. Since the difference over sex was
moderate only (11 per cent units), and the number of
females in each category was quite low (14 vs. 8), the
tendency obtained should be treated with reservation.
This recommendation is further motivated by the lack of
sex differences in both Paivio & Lambert's (1981) study
on bilingual coding and our own lateralization findings
in Chapter II. In addition, Fairweather (1976), in a
review of the relation between sex and various language
skills, has claimed that "there are few convincing sex
differences, either overall, or in interactions with
(putative) functional localization" (p. 231). Hence,

---

38. Incidentally, the fact that there were nearly four
times as many males as females who showed aphasic
disturbances (most of whom as a consequence of unilateral
lesions) seems to endorse the previous suggestion that
males tend to be somewhat more lateralized than females
(pp. 17-18). One should keep in mind, however, that
this lop-sided distribution is probably contingent to
some extent upon males' generally greater likelihood of
sustaining cerebral damage – for example in the capacity
of soldiers or holders of other dangerous occupations
(cf. Luria, 1970).

taking the aggregate weight of these indications into
account, it seems wisest to view the sex factor as
having no significant influence on the interlingual
functional relationship in the brain.

Age: As explained in Chapter II, analyses of the age
factor in behavioural language research are often impeded
by the fact that it tends to interact with other relevant
factors, in particular language proficiency. This makes
it hard to perform an accurate evaluation of the effect
of age, since we are likely to measure other aspects of
the individual's neuropsychological state as well. For
further treatment of this issue, the reader is therefore
referred primarily to the following discussion of the
factor of L2-proficiency, in which the age factor presumably is nested (p. 118 f.).

Yet, if we want to attempt a preliminary appraisal
now, we may utilize the aphasiological data from Albert &
Obler (1978) once more. In this study (where verbal proficiency was not controlled), the patients were classified
as young if they were under 36 years of age, and as old
if they had passed this level. This dichotomizing resulted
in 23 individuals being placed in the young group and
85 in the old one. 19 young and 60 old patients evinced
differential aphasic disturbances over their languages
(83% and 71% respectively), whereas four young and 25
old patients showed parallel symptoms (17% and 29%
respectively). Couched in psychological terms, these
figures suggest that young individuals are on the
average slightly more coordinately organized in the
brain than corresponding old ones (cf. Vildomec (1963),
who implies a similar pattern).

It is uncertain, however, whether this (unreliable)
difference really reflects the effect of age - i.e. the
biological course from maturation to degeneration of the
brain - on linguistic organization, or whether some other
variable is responsible. For this reason, at this time,
we cannot say anything about the possible influence of
the age factor on interlingual relations.

3.2. Language-acquisitional factors

Age of acquiring L2: Turning to more explicitly
linguistic considerations, one factor of interest is the
age at which a person becomes bilingual. For example, it
has been suggested that if L2 is acquired simultaneously,
or at least fairly closely in time with L1 (early bilingualism), the languages will be organized in a primarily
compound fashion in the brain. Conversely, if L2 is acquired
substantially later than L1 (late bilingualism), a coordinate state is more likely to obtain (e.g. Beardsmore,
1974). This development is thought to be caused by
differential conditions of cerebral and cognitive maturity
during childhood versus adolescence or adulthood. It may
be that early bilinguals build up a relatively uniform
language organization because they are exposed to both
languages during the same phase of maturation, whereas
late bilinguals develop more separate language systems
by engaging successive maturational phases when acquiring
L1 and L2 (cf. p. 19). Simultaneous experiences would also,
logically speaking, be more likely to become associated or
connected in memory than those separated in time. One
might thus wonder whether there is any empirical evidence
to corroborate this hypothesized effect of L2-acquisition.

We have found six studies in the specialist literature
which deal with this issue. Four of these are compatible
with the notion that early bilinguals rely on a more
interdependent type of language organization in the brain
than late bilinguals (e.g. Lambert, 1969; Genesee et al.,
1978; Vaid & Lambert, 1979). One study (Paivio & Lambert,
1981) showed no differences of organization, whereas the
remaining one (Segalowitz & Lambert, 1969) yielded the
opposite results, with late bilinguals exhibiting more
interdependence than early ones. Taken together, these
findings indicate that in general early bilinguals are
relatively more compound than corresponding late
bilinguals. Hence, we conclude that age of acquiring L2
appears to be a relevant factor in the development of
different patterns of functional language organization
in bilinguals.

Manner of acquiring L2: Many researchers view manner
of L2-acquisition as the main factor behind different
types of interlingual organization in the brain. When
the distinction between coordinate and compound bilingualism was originally coined, it was based on the
implications of separate versus shared contexts of
language acquisition, where a coordinate state was seen
as the result of learning, say, one language at home and
another from peers, and a compound state as the consequence of interchangeable learning in both contexts.
In other words, the different types of organization were
regarded as a function of the extent to which the
languages were used to refer to the same environmental
events (Ervin & Osgood, 1954; see also Weinreich, 1953).
This reasoning rests on the assumption that the brain
compounds the linguistic information that is internalized
within a self-contained setting, and the number of such
settings engaged by each bilingual (usually one or two)
would thus be crucial to the degree of independence-
interdependence between his underlying language correlates.

More recently, various aspects of language acquisition
have been emphasized in different studies. For example,
some scholars have focused on the organizational effects
of geographical-cultural differences of learning (e.g.
Lambert et al., 1958), others on the consequences of
communicational versus metalinguistic differences (e.g.
Krashen, 1981), or even differences of input modality
(e.g. Lambert et al., 1968). Here, however, we will
not analyze any of these subordinate components, but
only the general influence of separate versus shared
contexts, since this seems to be the most feasible and
commonly employed approach to the problem.

In testing whether manner of L2-acquisition is
important to interlingual organization, we located 10
studies of relevance. Seven of these endorsed the Ervin &
Osgood (1954) theory that separate acquisitional settings
for the bilinguals' languages engender more independence
between the language systems than do fused settings (e.g.
Lambert & Fillenbaum, 1959; Gekoski, 1970; Stafford, 1968).
Three studies showed no differences (Albert & Obler, 1978;

Gekoski, 1969; Olton, 1960), but no diametrically opposing
evidence to the present theory was found.

The accumulated research findings thus suggest that
when the acquisitional contexts are separate, there is a
higher probability for a coordinate state of language
organization to develop, and conversely when the contexts
are fused, there is a corresponding tendency in favour of
compound organization. Consequently, this conclusion
means that we ought to take manner of L2-acquisition
into account in discussions of independence versus interdependence of language in bilinguals.

Proficiency in L2: Another factor is proficiency in
L2. One theory regarding this variable states that in
the initial stages of acquisition, L2 is relatively
closely associated with the structures of L1, but that
with increasing proficiency, there is a progressive
development for the languages to become more functionally
separate in the brain (e.g. Riegel, 1968). This may be
due to non-fluent bilinguals having control of fewer
processing strategies in L2. They would therefore have
to utilize the knowledge of L1 more than fluent bilinguals.
Such an approach may entail extended cross-language
connections, or interdependent organization, which later,
as the learner improves, are superseded by more appropriate
intralanguage couplings, implying a more independent state
(cf. Albert & Obler, 1978).

In general, the above prediction is corroborated by
the research data. Of 12 pertinent studies, eight seem
to support the notion of a gradual development from a
compound to a coordinate state with increasing proficiency
in L2 (e.g. Goggin & Wickens, 1971; Dommergues & Lane,
1976; Davis & Wertheimer, 1967). Three investigations
showed no differences of organization between fluent and
non-fluent bilinguals (Kintsch & Kintsch, 1969; Obler &
Albert, 1978; Taylor, 1976b), whereas only one study
(Ervin, 1961) reported findings that contradicted the
general pattern, with an inferred development from a
coordinate to a compound state with increasing L2-
proficiency.

Apparently, then, the majority of invoked evidence espouses the hypothesized shift from a compound to a coordinate type of language organization as the level of L2-proficiency is enhanced. This means that also proficiency in L2 seems to be a significant factor in the establishment of functional relations between the languages in bilinguals.

3.3. Language-specific factors

Structural similarity between L1 and L2: Finally, we will discuss the potential influence of structural similarity between the bilinguals' languages. This concept is used here to cover the whole range of linguistic strata, i.e. phonological, morphological, lexical, and syntactical similarities, as well as general acoustic and graphic resemblances.

A number of investigations of linguistic functioning in the brain have shown that languages are coded primarily by meaning in memory (see Kintsch (1977) for a review). Semantic characteristics are however not the universally prevailing parameter – surface features seem to matter too. That this is the case has in particular been suggested by certain bilingual Stroop tests, where cross-language interference has obtained as a function of structural similarity. The greater the similarity between two languages, the more interference, has been the general pattern (e.g. Lambert & Preston, 1967).

On the basis of these findings, it may be hypothesized that the degree of interlingual surface correspondences influences the functional relation between the languages in the brain. If there is a great number of similar or common forms and structures, for example as in English and Swedish, a more compound type of organization seems likely to develop than if the languages are structurally disparate, for example as in English and Chinese. Logically, this difference would be the consequence of the brain using surface structure as an ancillary coding

attribute, complementing that of meaning, where similar
material both within and across languages tends to
cluster more than corresponding dissimilar material
(cf. Albert & Obler, 1978).

In trying to evaluate the present theory, we found
nine studies which dealt either explicitly or implicitly
with the matter. Seven of these corroborated the notion
that bilinguals show a relatively more compound organization in the brain if their languages are similar than if
they are dissimilar (e.g. MacKay & Bowman, 1969; LoCoco,
1975; Taylor, 1976b), whereas two studies yielded no
differences over this factor (Potter et al., 1984;
Scarborough et al., 1984). No diametrically opposing
data was found. The evidence adduced thus largely
supports the hypothesized similarity effect, and we
must therefore conclude that linguistic surface structure
seems to act as yet another significant conditioner of
functional language organization.

Concisely put, then, we have briefly examined clinical
and experimental data on seven circumstantial factors,
which may affect the way in which two languages are
mutually organized in the brain. Considerable evidence
was advanced for the relevance of the factors age of
acquiring L2, manner of acquiring L2, proficiency in L2,
and structural similarity between L1 and L2, while it
remains generally unresolved whether hand preference,
sex, and age have any measurable effect in this context.

4. Number choice test

Let us now turn to the presentation of our first
experiment on language interdependence - the number
choice test. As outlined above, the aim of this investigation is to shed some light on the functional relation
between the language-specific morphological systems in
the brain of Swedish-English subsidiary bilinguals, and
to relate possible differences across subjects and

stimuli to different circumstantial factors. To achieve
this, we will try to map the extent of interlingual
interference that obtains in inflectional morphology,
or to be precise, the amount of influence that the
Swedish plural formation system exercises in the receptive
processing of English singular and plural nouns. Attention
will be focused primarily on the potential effects of
some of the factors discussed in Section 3, viz. proficiency in L2, structural similarity between L1 and L2
(divided into inflectional and lexical similarity), sex,
and age.

The first measure to be taken in this endeavour was
to design an appropriate test paradigm. As stimuli, a
body of English nouns were selected which were completely
crossed over three variables - viz. number, plural form of
and lexical similarity to the Swedish translation equivalent - to form a stimulus matrix where the degree of
theoretical processing difficulty - i.e. the likelihood
of interlingual interference - differed systematically
over the cells. The test material thus ranged from
singular nouns which were both inflectionally and lexically
similar to their Swedish equivalents, via all possible
intermediate combinations, to plural nouns where the
inflectional and lexical properties were dissimilar across
language. Apart from this controlled variation, the stimuli
were carefully matched in several respects in order to
create equivalent testing conditions and thereby minimize
any inadequate sampling effects.

Moreover, the test population consisted of the same
subjects as those taking part in the previous lateralization experiments. The participants were thus all young
Swedes who were learning English at school as a foreign
language. They were divided into three different groups
on the basis of proficiency level in English (and age),
and in each of these groups, there was an equal number
of males and females.

The test method, finally, was a computerized version
of the common two-choice identification task (cf. the
designs reviewed by Paivio & Begg, 1981, Chapter 7).
Subjects were required to determine as quickly and

accurately as possible the form (singular or plural) of
a series of successively presented English nouns by
means of pressing one of two response buttons. Both the
processing time (latency) and the truth-value of each
response were recorded during this performance, meaning
that we had access to two different potential parameters
of stimulus difficulty. Long latencies and many errors
in dealing with a particular type of stimuli were taken
as evidence for a greater processing difficulty with this
material - presumably caused by interlingual interference
primarily - than with other types of stimuli yielding
shorter latencies and fewer errors. The latency data were
however regarded as the primary parameter, since it is a
more flexible and therefore a more sensitive measure than
that of error rate. (For a more detailed description of
the stimuli and the experimental method, see Section 4.2;
for a similar description of the subjects, see Section
4.2 in Chapter II.)

Below, we will draw up a number of hypotheses concerning the outcome of the present experiment. These
predictions, which are based on the expected effects or
non-effects of the factorial design over stimuli and
subjects, will constitute our working hypotheses in the
test and serve as guidelines for the postexperimental
statistical treatment of the recorded data.

4.1. Hypotheses

As we have seen, there are several studies which
indicate that the factor of structural similarity between
L1 and L2 influences the way in which the bilingual brain
is functionally organized. Similar languages seem to
entail a more interdependent organization of the underlying language processes than do dissimilar ones (see pp.
119-120). This means that the probability of similar
languages activating each other and thereby causing
mutual interference should be higher than when the
languages are dissimilar. One may thus expect that a

certain amount of systematic interference will obtain
between Swedish and English, since a considerable degree
of similarity exists between them.

If we push this matter further and distinguish between
similar and dissimilar material also within the same pair
of languages, a corresponding effect is said to obtain –
i.e. that interlingually similar material is functionally
more connected than dissimilar (e.g. Taylor, 1976b).
According to this view, the influence of structural
likeness would add to the associative effect of conceptual
(semantic) similarity that always seems to occur between
translation equivalents. The central question here, then,
is whether this phenomenon is demonstrable in Swedish-
English bilinguals processing English nouns.

But let us first take a cursory look at the character
of the plural formation systems in Swedish and English.
As a rule, both languages indicate plurality by means of
a suffix. While the English system is quite regular on
this account, with an almost exclusive use of either -s
or -es, the Swedish system is more variable as in addition
to the predominant suffixes -ar, -or, and -er, it frequently
also employs the zero plural (on nouns in the neuter).
The natural consequence of this is that there exist both
pairs of translation equivalents which exhibit similar
plural inflection (both languages use a suffix, e.g.
boat - boats vs. båt - båtar) and such which do not
(English uses a suffix but not Swedish, e.g. house - houses
vs. hus - hus).[39]

If we combine the distinction of inflectional similarity
with a similar one of lexical similarity - e.g. door - dörr
vs. table - bord - we may achieve a means to test how
inflectional processing is carried out in the brain and
whether this activity is dependent on lexical structure.
This connection seems intuitively plausible, since
logically a close relation between words in general and

---

39. There are a few English nouns with the zero plural
as well, e.g. aircraft, deer, and salmon. This type of
inflection is however quite rare, and we will therefore
disregard it in the present context.

their possible inflections must be postulated.

The basic assumption of our experiment is thus that similar items across language are more likely to prime (indirectly activate) each other than dissimilar ones, because they are more closely organized neuropsychologically. On the basis of this, we may predict the following. An English noun which is lexically similar to its Swedish translation equivalent will activate not only its own inflectional rules, but also prime those of the Swedish system, and if the plural formation then corresponds over the languages, i.e. both use a plural suffix, this will facilitate the identification of the number of the noun, but if they differ, i.e. one uses a suffix but not the other, there will occur some interference in the form of response inhibition or distraction, because the Swedish inflectional rules give conflicting information in relation to the English. On the other hand, if a noun and its translation equivalent are lexically dissimilar, the effect of inflectional congruence versus incongruence will not be equally strong, because the cross-language lexical priming, if any, is considerably weaker in this case and therefore does not activate the Swedish inflectional system to the same extent. The priming effect that obtains here will instead be caused principally by the factor of conceptual similarity.

Hence, from this argument, we may formulate two hypotheses as to the prospective results of the present experiment. Hypothesis I states that incongruent inflections between English nouns and their Swedish translation equivalents will engender more response interference than congruent inflections. Hypothesis II states that the effect of the inflectional relation between the languages will be a function of lexical similarity in such a way that the greatest amount of interference occurs when the nouns and their translation equivalents are lexically similar but inflectionally dissimilar, and the least amount when they are both lexically and inflectionally similar. Lexically dissimilar forms will fall in-between these, with incongruent inflections yielding more interference than congruent ones also in this category.

Moreover, we know that the degree of linguistic interdependence in the brain may be influenced by different levels of proficiency in L2. As was shown in the previous section, eight of 12 consulted studies supported the notion that there is a gradual transition from a relatively interdependent to a more independent state of language organization with increasing L2-proficiency (see pp. 118-119). Since the subjects in the present experiment represented three different proficiency levels in L2, it is reasonable to expect a similar pattern here. This effect, which probably reflects the possible influence of subject age as well (cf. Chapter II), would take the form of more cross-language inflectional inter-ference in low-proficient subjects than in those who have become linguistically more advanced. Hypothesis III thus predicts that the degree of interference between the Swedish and English plural formation systems will decrease with increasing age/English proficiency level in our subjects.

Lastly, no reliable indications in favour of any effects of sex in this context have been found. Though a tendency for females to be slightly more interdependent than males was demonstrated in our previous review (see pp. 113-115), this evidence was too weak to suggest anything but that sex generally is irrelevant to how the brain is functionally organized, and thus to how much interlingual interference occurs there. Hypothesis IV accordingly states that there will be no essential difference between the amounts of interference that males and females exhibit.

4.2. Description

Stimuli: Three independent binary variables were combined to produce a 2 x 2 x 2 design with eight different experimental conditions. The variables were (1) number (singular vs. plural form[40], e.g. boy vs. boys), (2) plural form of the Swedish translation equi-

valent (suffix vs. no suffix, e.g. <u>boll</u> - <u>bollar</u> (<u>ball</u> -
<u>balls</u>) vs. <u>skepp</u> - <u>skepp</u> (<u>ship</u> - <u>ships</u>)), and (3) lexical
similarity to the Swedish translation equivalent (similar
vs. dissimilar, e.g. <u>hat</u> - <u>hatt</u> vs. <u>girl</u> - <u>flicka</u>). The
resulting matrix was filled with 40 English nouns, all of
which were considered to have natural and easily evoked
Swedish translation equivalents, yielding five nouns in
each cell (see Figure 12 and Appendix).

<u>Figure 12</u>

The stimulus matrix used in the number choice test.

	similar	dissimilar
singular Swe. plural suffix	1A ring (ring)	1B girl (flicka)
singular no Swe. plural suffix	2A ship (skepp)	2B beard (skägg)
plural Swe. plural suffix	3A lamps (lampor)	3B birds (fåglar)
plural no Swe. plural suffix	4A eggs (ägg)	4B saints (helgon)

Another body of 40 English nouns was also included
in the stimuli. These words did however not belong to the
matrix, but served as controls only in order to distract
the subjects during the test. In particular, they all
contained a stem-final <u>s</u>, for example as in <u>bus</u> and <u>gases</u>
(the nouns in the matrix had a stem-final non-<u>s</u>), and
were used to prevent the subjects from adopting a
processing strategy based only on the presence or
absence of a final <u>s</u>. The presence of such an <u>s</u> might
otherwise lead to a mechanical <u>plural</u> response, initiated
by the overwhelmingly high frequency of the final <u>s</u> as
plural indicator, whereas the absence of it might lead
to a mechanical <u>singular</u> response. There were 20 singular
and 20 plural nouns in this category.

The classification of the stimuli over the variable
lexical similarity was effected on the basis of writing

---

40. Only nouns with the regular plural suffixes -<u>s</u> and
-<u>es</u> were used.

similarities between the languages. Each noun was
arbitrarily judged by the experimenter to be either
similar or dissimilar to its translation equivalent,
and all dubious cases in-between were discarded.

Frequency and length of the stimuli were also taken
into account during the selection process. Homogeneity
over both these parameters was desired, since variation
between the different cells in terms of frequency and
length scores are liable to produce experimental artifacts.
Using the Kučera & Francis (1967) count of word frequency,
the selected nouns were found to be of roughly equal
frequency over the cells, and this also applied to the
factor of word-length, within which a notable difference
was observed between singular and plural nouns only
(mean lengths = 4.4 and 6.0 letters respectively).
The stimuli appeared in white uppercase letters on a
dark background, with each stimulus letter measuring
1.0 cm in height and .5 cm in width.

Apparatus: A BASIC programme for the execution of the
experiment was prepared and loaded into a Heath Z-89
computer. Governed by the programme, the computer carried
out five different routines: (1) Independent randomization
of the nouns across subjects, (2) presentation of the
nouns on a video screen, (3) timing and registration of
subjects' response latencies (msec), (4) registration
of subjects' responses, i.e. singular or plural, and
(5) determination and registration of the truth-value
of subjects' responses, i.e. correct or incorrect.

The randomization and timing processes were executed
by a random-number unit and an electronic timer ($\pm$ 1 msec)
respectively in the computer. The presentation of the
stimuli was done on an external Luxor 24" b/w video
screen, previously used in our visual lateralization
experiment. Further, responses were recorded and fed
into the computer by means of two identical hand-held
response buttons, operated by the thumb of each hand.
One button was connected to the response singular
and the other to the response plural. The left-
right orientation of the response buttons was

counterbalanced across subjects, and for each subject
it was also marked by two signs, indicating which hand
held the singular button and which held the plural one.

Procedure: All subjects were tested individually in
a quiet, semidarkened room. They were seated in front
of the video screen at a distance of approximately 1.1
metre, and the response buttons were placed in their
left and right hand respectively. Each subject received
the following instructions orally in Swedish. "The
present experiment is an attempt to shed some light on
how English nouns are processed in the brain of native
Swedish speakers. You will see the nouns one at a time
on the screen in front of you and your task is to decide
as quickly as possible whether they are in the singular
or in the plural form. If a noun is in the singular form,
press the button marked singular; if a noun is in the
plural form, press the button marked plural. Your
decisions must be fast and accurate, and if you don't
know which response is the correct one, guess. No feedback about the correctness of your responses will be
given during the test, and no opportunity to change
any of them is offered."[41]

Subjects then received a practice block of 10 nouns,
which were not included in the test material. This
session served to "warm the participants up" before
the test and to make sure that they had grasped the
instructions fully.

The actual test started with an independent randomization of all the 80 nouns by the computer. When a noun
was exposed on the screen, both the response buttons
and the electronic timer were activated. The noun stayed

---

41. A pilot experiment tested feedback of response
truth-value following each trial. It was found that
such a procedure made the subjects lose concentration
in case of an error, and had in general only a disturbing
influence on the test. Feedback was therefore discarded
in the present experiment as well as in the subsequent
one (the tense choice test).

on the screen until one of the response buttons was
pressed and simultaneously the timer stopped. The
computer stored the response, determined and stored
its latency and its truth-value, and then exposed a
new noun on the screen (interstimulus time = 1.2
seconds). The test was performed without any pauses
and took approximately four minutes.

4.3. Results

The experimental results were subjected to three
different statistical analyses, viz. cell-difference
computations on both latencies and error data, and a
correlation test between these two parameters. Each
analysis will be dealt with separately below.

Latencies: The latency data[42] from the present experiment is summarized in Table 11.

---

42. The data from the present test, as well as from the
following tense choice test, contain latencies from both
correct and incorrect responses. Prima facie, this pooling
may strike the reader as inadequate, as erroneous responses
are incorporated into the data, but there are two good
reasons for it. First, stimulus processing is supposed
to be of a similar type whether the following decision
relating to it is correct or not. Theoretically, a stimulus
goes through the same linguistic comparisons and is subject
to the same amount of interference irrespective of which
response button is eventually pressed. Accordingly, error
latencies should reflect stimulus difficulty as well as
correct response latencies do. Second, if error latencies
were excluded from the analysis, the cells containing
the most difficult stimuli would suffer a greater loss
of data than the comparatively easy ones. Although the
overall error rate was rather low, this might result
in uneven statistical comparisons and thus in the introduction of an unnecessary factor of uncertainty.

INTERDEPENDENCE

Table 11

Mean latencies (msec) in each experimental condition, on each value of the within-subject variables, and for singular and plural controls in the noun test.

	Group A			Group B			Group C			
	M	F	Tot.	M	F	Tot.	M	F	Tot.	Total
cell 1A	686	773	730	704	722	713	582	630	606	683
cell 2A	769	844	806	644	644	644	597	661	629	693
cell 3A	805	937	871	727	766	747	656	664	660	759
cell 4A	834	1038	936	777	804	791	640	666	653	793
cell 1B	678	719	698	639	695	667	601	632	617	661
cell 2B	730	877	803	653	678	666	599	626	613	694
cell 3B	812	902	857	785	847	816	672	630	651	775
cell 4B	891	1110	1001	748	789	769	634	652	643	804
singular	716	803	759	660	685	672	595	637	616	683
plural	836	997	916	759	801	780	651	653	652	783
Swe. suf.	746	832	789	714	757	735	628	639	634	719
no Swe. suf.	806	967	887	706	729	717	618	651	634	746
similar	774	898	836	713	734	723	619	655	637	732
dissimilar	778	902	840	706	752	729	626	635	631	733
Total	776	900	838	710	742	726	623	645	634	732
sing. contr.	873	1022	948	770	832	801	693	708	700	816
plur. contr.	790	1020	905	840	926	883	672	707	689	826
Tot. contr.	831	1021	926	805	879	842	682	707	695	821
Grand Total	803	961	882	757	811	784	653	676	664	777

M = males, F = females

   In the figures below, the main parts of the numerical information in Table 11 are reproduced graphically.
   Evidently, there is a substantial variation in the latency data, both within the separate variables and over the different cells of the stimulus matrix. The curves in the figures are essentially parallel, although they display a slightly disordinal relation in some instances, and there is an almost linear decrease of latency from Group A to Group C. The greatest variation seems to exist within the variables of number and age/English proficiency level, and between controls and matrix nouns, while the curves for Swedish plural form (except

Figure 13

Mean latencies for singular and plural nouns as a function of age/English proficiency level in the noun test.

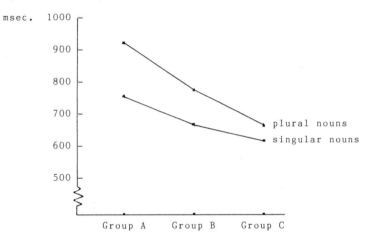

Figure 14

Mean latencies for nouns with and without a plural suffix on the Swedish translation equivalents as a function of age/English proficiency level in the noun test.

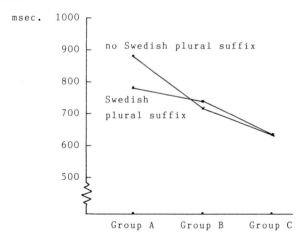

Figure 15

Mean latencies for nouns with lexically similar
and dissimilar Swedish translation equivalents as a
function of age/English proficiency level in the
noun test.

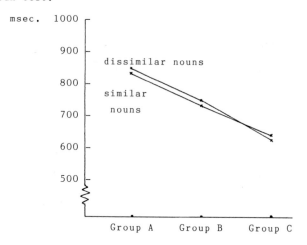

Figure 16

Mean latencies for males and females as a function
of age/English proficiency level in the noun test.

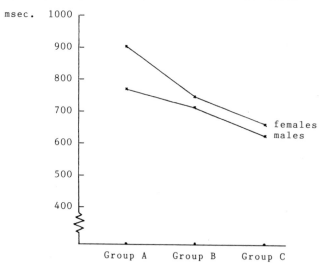

Figure 17

Mean latencies for the three age/English proficiency
groups as a function of experimental condition in the
noun test.

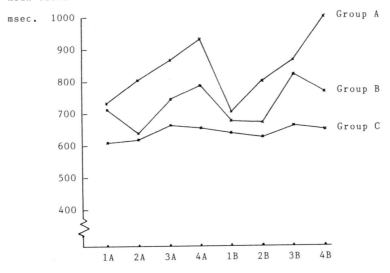

Figure 18

Mean latencies for controls and matrix nouns, i.e. nouns
with and without a stem-final s, as a function of age/English
proficiency level in the noun test.

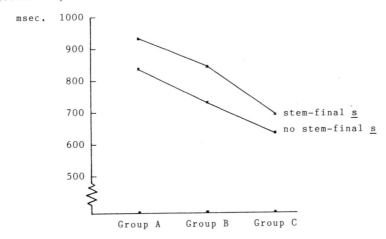

Group A) and lexical similarity more or less coincide
respectively.

A five-way analysis of variance with repeated measures
with age/English proficiency level (3) and sex (2) as
between-subject variables and number (2), plural form
of the Swedish translation equivalent (2), and lexical
similarity to the Swedish translation equivalent (2) as
within-subject variables was performed on the material
to test the reliability of the observed trends. The
following three significant main effects emerged.
Age/English proficiency level. The latencies decreased
with increasing age/proficiency level, i.e. Group A
had the longest mean response time (838 msec), Group B
was intermediate (726 msec), and Group C had the shortest
mean response time (634 msec), (F(2,54)=9.9, p<.01).
Number. Singular nouns were identified faster than
plural ones (mean latencies = 683 msec vs. 783 msec),
(F(1,54)=38.1, p<.01). Plural form of the Swedish translation equivalent. Incongruent plural forms over language
generally produced longer latencies than congruent plural
forms, i.e. nouns with a suffix on the Swedish equivalent
were responded to faster than those without such a suffix
(mean latencies = 719 msec vs. 746 msec), (F(1,54)=7.0,
p<.05).

No effect of sex occurred. Although males were on the
average somewhat faster than females (703 msec vs. 762
msec), this difference did not reach significance.

There were also two significant two-way interactions.
Number x age/English proficiency level. The latency
difference between singular and plural nouns declined
with age/proficiency level, i.e. Group A had a mean
difference of 157 msec, Group B 108 msec, and Group C
35 msec, (F(2,54)=4.7, p<.05). Plural form of the Swedish
translation equivalent x age/English proficiency level.
Group A exhibited a substantial difference between
congruent and incongruent plural forms, i.e. nouns with
a suffix on the Swedish translation equivalent were
identified faster than nouns without such a suffix (mean
difference = 98 msec), while Group B and Group C displayed
a rough equivalence between these two conditions (mean

differences = 18 msec and 1 msec respectively), (F(2,54=
12.6, p<.01). No other interactions reached significance.

In addition, post hoc comparisons (analyses of variance)
were made between the latencies of controls and matrix
nouns, i.e. nouns with and without a stem-final s, and
between singular and plural controls. It was found that
it took significantly longer time to respond to the nouns
from the control category than to the matrix nouns (mean
latencies = 821 msec vs. 732 msec), (F(1,54)=27.7, p<.01).
There was however no significant latency difference between
singular and plural nouns with a stem-final s (mean latencies
= 816 msec and 826 msec respectively), (F(1,54)=.4, p=.55).

Errors: The error data from the present experiment is
summarized in Table 12.

Table 12

Mean error rate (%)[43] in each experimental condition,
on each value of the within-subject variables, and for
singular and plural controls in the noun test.

	Group A			Group B			Group C			
	M	F	Tot.	M	F	Tot.	M	F	Tot.	Total
cell 1A	2.0	0	1.0	0	2.0	1.0	0	0	0	.7
cell 2A	2.0	6.0	4.0	6.0	0	3.0	0	4.0	2.0	3.0
cell 3A	12.0	14.0	13.0	2.0	6.0	4.0	12.0	8.0	10.0	9.0
cell 4A	12.0	12.0	12.0	4.0	6.0	5.0	2.0	4.0	3.0	6.7
cell 1B	2.0	0	1.0	0	0	0	2.0	0	1.0	.7
cell 2B	0	4.0	2.0	2.0	2.0	2.0	0	0	0	1.3
cell 3B	6.0	8.0	7.0	2.0	2.0	2.0	4.0	4.0	4.0	4.3
cell 4B	10.0	6.0	8.0	0	4.0	2.0	6.0	2.0	4.0	4.7
singular	1.5	2.5	2.0	2.0	1.0	1.5	.5	1.0	.8	1.4

(Continued on the next page.)

43. The fact that the overall error rate was quite low
(4.1%) implies that subjects guessed only exceptionally
while carrying out the task (cf. the similar value of the
following verb test). If all responses had been random
guesses, which might have been the case if subjects were
not serious about the test, the error rate would have been
around 50%. Obviously, then, this did not occur here.

Table 12 (continued)

	Group A			Group B			Group C			
	M	F	Tot.	M	F	Tot.	M	F	Tot.	Total
plural	10.0	10.0	10.0	2.0	4.5	3.3	6.0	4.5	5.3	6.2
Swe. suf.	5.5	5.5	5.5	1.0	2.5	1.8	4.5	3.0	3.8	3.7
no Swe. suf.	6.0	7.0	6.5	3.0	3.0	3.0	2.0	2.5	2.3	3.9
similar	7.0	8.0	7.5	3.0	3.5	3.3	3.5	4.0	3.8	4.8
dissimilar	4.5	4.5	4.5	1.0	2.0	1.5	3.0	1.5	2.3	2.8
Total	5.8	6.3	6.0	2.0	2.8	2.4	3.3	2.8	3.0	3.8
sing. contr.	12.5	7.0	9.8	4.0	6.5	5.3	6.0	5.0	5.5	6.8
plur. contr.	3.5	4.0	3.8	1.5	1.5	1.5	2.0	.5	1.3	2.2
Tot. contr.	8.0	5.5	6.8	2.8	4.0	3.4	4.0	2.8	3.4	4.5
Grand Total	6.9	5.9	6.4	2.4	3.4	2.9	3.6	2.8	3.2	4.1

M = males, F = females

In the following figures, the main error data in Table 12 is rendered graphically.

Figure 19

Mean error rates for singular and plural nouns as a function of age/English proficiency level in the noun test.

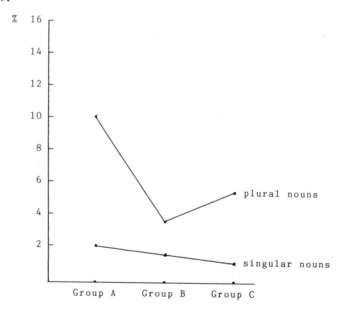

Figure 20

Mean error rates for nouns with and without a plural suffix on the Swedish translation equivalent as a function of age/English proficiency level in the noun test.

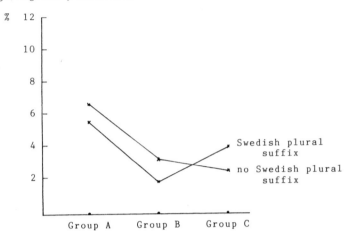

Figure 21

Mean error rates for nouns with lexically similar and dissimilar Swedish translation equivalents as a function of age/English proficiency level in the noun test.

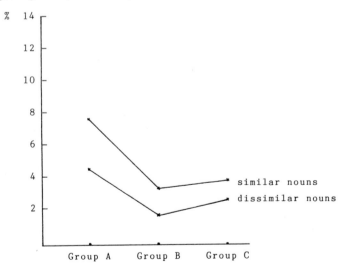

Figure 22

Mean error rates for males and females as a function of age/English proficiency level in the noun test.

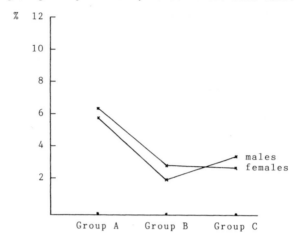

Figure 23

Mean error rates for the three age/English proficiency groups as a function of experimental condition in the noun test.

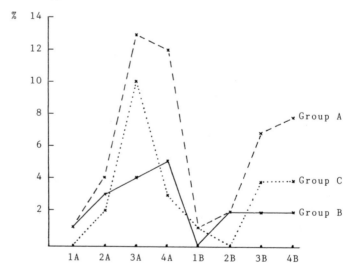

Figure 24

Mean error rates for controls and matrix nouns, i.e.
nouns with and without a stem-final s, as a function of
age/English proficiency level in the noun test.

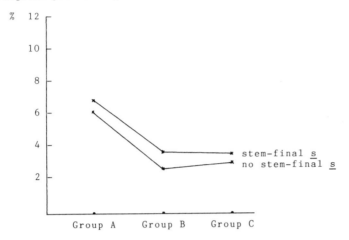

As can be seen, not quite the same neat linearity and
parallelism as obtained in the latency analyses are
present in the error data. The non-linearity is caused
primarily by the fact that Group B tended to surpass
Group C on the task (cf. the mean error rates 2.4% and
3.0% respectively). This outcome gives rise to the
slightly V-shaped curves seen in the figures above.
Some instances of lack of parallelism may also be noted.
Both the variables of number and age/English proficiency
level display irregular curve patterns, with a substantial
separation within Group A and Group C over the former
and a complex intertwining of Group B and Group C over
the latter.

A five-way analysis of variance with repeated measures
involving the same variables as the corresponding latency
analysis was performed on the error data. Three significant
main effects emerged: Age/English proficiency level.
Group A made more errors than Group B and Group C (mean
error rates = 6.0%, 2.4%, and 3.0% respectively), $(F(2,54)=$
6.8, $p<.01$). Number. Plural nouns engendered more errors

than singular nouns (mean error rates = 6.2% vs. 1.4%),
(F(1,54)=37.6, p<.01). <u>Lexical similarity to the Swedish
translation equivalent</u>. More incorrect responses were
made to lexically similar nouns than to dissimilar ones
(mean error rates = 4.8% vs. 2.8%), (F(1,54)=6.5, p<.05).

The effect of sex, i.e. the difference of error rate
between males and females (3.7% vs. 4.0%), was not strong
enough to reach significance.

In addition, there was one significant two-way interaction: <u>Number x age/English proficiency level</u>. The mean
difference of error rate between singular and plural
nouns decreased from Group A (8.0%) to Group C (4.5%)
to Group B (1.8%), (F(2,54)=5.5, p<.01). No other interactions reached significance.

A test similar to that of the latency analysis was
also done on the error rate difference between controls
and matrix nouns and between singular and plural controls.
Nouns with a stem-final <u>s</u> were found to cause a slightly,
but not significantly, higher incidence of errors than
nouns without a stem-final <u>s</u> (mean error rates = 4.5%
vs. 3.8%), (F(1,54)=2.4, p=.13). The error rate difference
between singular and plural controls was however highly
significant - singular nouns with a stem-final <u>s</u> produced
more errors than the corresponding plural ones (mean
error rates = 6.8% vs. 2.2%), (F(1,54)=26.7, p<.01).

<u>Latencies - errors</u>: Since we have treated both latency
and error rate as potential parameters of stimulus
difficulty, it would also be of interest to see whether
these measures correlate to any extent, i.e. whether
they reflect interference and other difficulty aspects
similarly. A correlation test (Fisher's Z-method) was
therefore conducted between the latency and error data,
in which both overall and group-specific correlation
were probed.[44]

---

44. Those subjects (=15) who did not make any errors in
the test were of course excluded from this analysis. The
remaining subject sample thus consisted of 45 individuals
(18 in Group A, 12 in Group B, and 15 in Group C).

Contrary to expectations, the overall Z-coefficient was found to be very close to zero (-.004), thus suggesting an almost total mutual independence between latencies and error scores when the data are pooled over age/English proficiency level.

If we look at the three separate groups of subjects, however, different patterns emerge: Group A had a Z-coefficient of .12, Group B 0, and Group C -.14, and a subsequent test of significance further revealed that these intergroup differences were significant ($F(2,42)=4.8$, $p<.05$). Obviously, then, there is a trend from a positive to a negative relationship between latency and error rate as the level of age/English proficiency level increases. In Group A, the positive value of the Z-coefficient is to be interpreted as showing on the average a certain increase of the error rate when the latencies increase, or conversely, a decrease of the error rate when the latencies decrease. In Group B, no inter-relation at all appears to be present, i.e. latency and error rate seem to be independent of each other. In Group C, the pattern is reversed from that of Group A, with a small decrease of the error rate when the latencies increase, or conversely, an increase of the error rate when the latencies decrease.

4.4. Discussion

Using the joint results of the latency and error rate analyses, we may now try to evaluate the hypotheses drawn up before the experiment started. For the sake of convenience, the discussion will be divided into within-subject and between-subject considerations. This will also include a few words about the other effects that obtained in the analyses, which in themselves do not concern any of the hypotheses.

Within-subject effects: The most interesting effect that emerged from the stimulus matrix was that of plural

<u>form of the Swedish translation equivalent</u> (latencies).
As noted before, it shows that stimulus nouns with
incongruent plural formation in relation to their
Swedish translation equivalents yielded longer latencies
than such with congruent formation. This finding suggests
that subjects experienced more difficulty in identifying
the number of the nouns in which there was conflicting
inflectional information across language than in those
cases where this information corresponded. The Swedish
inflectional system thus seems to have exercised a
certain amount of inhibition or interference in the
processing of the "interference-loaded" portion of the
stimuli.

No analogous trend was observed over the error parameter, though, and this was probably because the interference effect was not strong enough to influence this
grosser measure. At any rate, the prediction of Hypothesis
I that there would occur more interference when the plural
markers did not match is confirmed by the present latency
data.

Hypothesis II, on the other hand, was not supported
by either of our two parameters. As we remember, this
prediction stated that the effect of inflectional
congruence would be a function of lexical similarity
in such a way that the amount of interference decreased
gradually over the conditions lexical similarity/inflec-
tional dissimilarity - lexical and inflectional dissimilarity - lexical dissimilarity/inflectional similarity
- lexical and inflectional similarity. The closest we
came to such an interaction, however, was a significant
main effect of <u>lexical similarity to the Swedish translation equivalent</u> (errors), indicating that lexical
similarity across language yielded more errors or interference than lexical dissimilarity irrespective of
inflectional correspondence. (There was no such effect
of latency, though.) This seems to mean that the factor
of lexical similarity was not related to the amount of
inflectional interference that obtained.

Trying to explain the above effect, it is conceivable
that a certain portion of it was due to subjects, while

processing the lexically similar stimuli, experiencing
a greater amount of inhibition in the inflectionally
incongruent conditions than facilitation in the corresponding congruent ones. This material as a whole thus
produced more interference than the lexically dissimilar
stimuli, which presumably yielded generally less cross-
language activity and thereby a smaller absolute
difference between inhibition and facilitation.

However, since the highest error rate in fact was
observed for a group of the similar, congruent nouns
(cell 3A), the present similarity effect probably
constitutes an experimental artifact primarily. It is
hard to pinpoint the answer as to why the lexically
similar stimuli should appear more difficult to process,
but the test data may have been influenced by subtle
differences, or combinations of differences, of word-
length, word-frequency, and unexpected individual
processing strategies. This possibility reminds us as
well that there is a certain risk of experimental
artifacts in all our within-subject comparisons of
different categories of stimuli, and that the present
stimulus effects, and such effects in general, therefore
should be treated with great circumspection, probably
greater than that which is needed in corresponding
between-subject comparisons.

That word-length, word-frequency, and processing
strategy are important factors in this context may also
be inferred from the performance differences reflected
by number (latencies) and number (errors). These effects,
which in fact were the strongest that obtained in the
whole experiment, show that plural nouns yielded both
longer latencies and more errors than singular ones.
There seem to be two main reasons for this outcome.

First, as the singular stimuli were on the average
1.6 letters shorter than the plural (see p. 127) and
uninflected forms normally are more frequent than inflected ones (e.g. Clark & Clark, 1977), it appears
natural that subjects found the plural conditions somewhat more difficult to deal with. The shorter the stimulus
and the more familiar individuals are with it, the easier

it should be to identify it and respond to it correctly.

Second, despite the precautions taken in selecting the
stimuli (see pp. 125-127), it is possible that subjects
were able to use a processing strategy based on the
presence and absence of a word-final s. Since almost all
English nouns indicate the plural form by means of an
-(e)s-suffix, subjects may have utilized the negative
implication of this fact and responded singular mechanically
to each stimulus that did not carry a final s. The consequence of this strategy would be that singular nouns
were responded to faster (and probably more accurately)
than plural ones. At least, this speculation is supported
by the results of our comparison between matrix and
control stimuli, in which it was found that singular
and plural nouns without a stem-final s (including 20
nouns with a word-final non-s) engendered significantly
shorter latencies than such with a stem-final s (all of
these accordingly having a word-final s).

Moreover, if the present s-strategy is real, it would
also explain why singular nouns with a stem-final s
(singular controls) yielded more errors than corresponding
plural ones (plural controls). Just as subjects tended to
respond singular when a stimulus lacked a word-final s,
they would have been more inclined to respond plural
when such an s was present. The conflicting cues from
singular nouns ending in s - i.e. the quasi-plural, final
s versus the true inflectional information about the
words - would then make it more difficult to identify
the number of these items and produce correct responses
to them.

Between-subject effects: If we proceed to the response
patterns across the different subject groups, further
notable performance differences emerge. As expected, the
swiftness and accuracy in identifying the number of the
stimulus nouns were essentially a function of age/English
proficiency level. With regard to latencies, the youngest
and least proficient subjects of Group A were slowest in
responding, the intermediate ones in Group B fell in-
between, and the oldest and most proficient subjects of

Group C were fastest (age/English proficiency level –
latencies; see Figure 17).

With regard to errors, the greatest number of incorrect
responses was found in Group A, but between Group B and
Group C the anticipated relation was reversed, with the
former showing a lower number of errors than the latter
(age/English proficiency level – errors; see Figure 23).
These trends are also reflected in the interactions
number x age/English proficiency level (latencies) and
number x age/English proficiency level (errors), which
indicate that both the latency and error rate differences
between singular and plural nouns generally decreased
with increasing age/proficiency level (see Figures 13
and 19). In other words, the overall processing difficulty
in the test, including the differences of this factor
between singular and plural stimuli, seem to have been
felt most strongly in Group A, less in Group B, and
least in Group C.

Arguably, this performance pattern, save the un-
accountably low error rate in Group B, constitutes a
logical consequence of the differences of L2-proficiency
and cognitive ability (the latter of which is presumably
conditioned by different levels of age and intellectual
capacity) that are thought to exist between our three
test groups. As proposed in Chapter II, the subjects of
Group B and in particular those of Group C appear to be
both intellectually more advanced and more experienced
readers and language users in general than those of
Group A, and it is therefore quite in order that they,
as measured by their faster and more accurate responses,
should find the experimental task as a whole easier to
carry out than less advanced subjects.

What is more important here, however, is that we also
recorded an effect of plural form of the Swedish translation equivalent x age/English proficiency level (latencies). This interaction means that Group A produced
considerably slower responses to nouns with incongruent
plural forms in relation to their Swedish equivalents
than to nouns showing inflectional congruence, whereas
practically no such congruence-incongruence difference

was seen in either Group B or Group C (see Figure 14).
The main cause for this trend seems to be that in the
processing of the incongruent stimuli by Group A, but
not by Group B and Group C, there occurred a certain
amount of interference from the Swedish inflectional
system, which made the subjects hesitate somewhat in the
identification of the number of the nouns and thereby
delayed their responses. This shows that the previously
demonstrated main effect of interference (plural form of
the Swedish translation equivalent - latencies) was
largely due to the response pattern produced by Group A.
The present latency effect thus confirms the prediction
of Hypothesis III that the degree of interference between
the Swedish and English plural formation systems would
decrease with increasing age/English proficiency level.
Interestingly enough, there was a similar tendency over
the error parameter, but this was obviously too weak to
reach statistical significance (see Figure 20).

Regarding the sex factor, no significant effects
emerged in our analyses. Males and females seem to
have been about equally sensitive to interference from
the Swedish inflectional system as measured by the
latencies and number of errors they produced while
carrying out the test task (see Figures 16 and 22).
This means that Hypothesis IV as well - i.e. that males
and females would exhibit similar patterns of inflectional
interference - is supported by the experimental data.

Incidentally, we may also note that an overall
speed-for-accuracy tradeoff occurred over sex. Whereas
males tended to make faster responses than females,
females were usually more accurate than males. This
implies that males were somewhat rasher than females
in making their responses - what they gained in speed,
they lost in accuracy, while for the apparently more
cautious females, it was the other way round - what they
lost in speed, they gained in accuracy (cf. Fairweather,
1976).

Finally, a few words may be said about the relation
between our two dependent measures - latency and error
rate. As we saw in the preceding section, there was

practically no overall correlation between these parameters, a finding which prima facie seems rather odd
taking into account that they both are thought to
reflect variations in stimulus difficulty. However,
as hinted at before, a partial explanation of this
unparallelism may be derived from the possibility that
error registration is too gross a measure to mirror
adequately the subtle interference effects that we
are interested in. Whereas the latency parameter is
a quasi-continuous and presumably quite sensitive
measure, the error rate parameter is only a coarse,
binary variable which logically cannot be as efficient
as that of latency in this context. The consequence of
this sensitivity difference may be that the functions of
our two parameters diverged more than was at first
expected. Most likely, the error data reflect primarily
subjects' ignorance of certain stimuli - i.e. the errors
were caused by defective guesswork - or the influence of
procedural difficulty, for example occasional confusion
of the response buttons (which in fact was reported
postexperimentally by some of the subjects), while the
latency data, apart from also containing a small component
of these effects, mirrored more of the deeper interference
processes and other subtle difficulty effects within and
between the different experimental conditions. This means
that the latency and error parameters may have recorded
performance effects that were engendered by different
difficulty factors, and it is then no surprise that these
data do not follow the same pattern. Thus, if this theory
is valid, it would explain at least to some extent why
latencies and error rates failed to correlate. It would,
moreover, justify our previous decision to use latency
as the primary parameter, superior to error rate, in
evaluating our experimental hypotheses, a preference
which is also motivated by the low overall error frequency,
the implications of which consequently should not be
given too much weight.

   If we summarize the present experiment, then, the
following points may be made.

(1) English nouns with incongruent plural form in relation to their Swedish translation equivalents seem to cause more cross-language inflectional interference than such with congruent form across language.

(2) The inflectional interference effect is apparently not a function of lexical similarity, since no appreciable inhibition or facilitation of subjects' responses through manipulation of this factor was achieved.

(3) More inflectional interference tends to obtain in young and low-proficient subjects than in older and more advanced ones, or in other words, the interference effect was a function of age/English proficiency level.

(4) Males and females seem to be about equally affected by inflectional interference.

We have deliberately omitted any attempts to give a deeper neuropsychological explanation of our demonstrated interference effects here. This endeavour will instead be undertaken subsequent to the next experiment, in which we, hopefully, will be able to assess and qualify the merit of the present findings.

5. Tense choice test

The other experiment here – the tense choice test – will also concern inflectional interference. Again, the objective is to find out how the underlying morphological systems are functionally related in our bilinguals, and in particular, whether this relation is influenced by structural similarity between the languages, proficiency in L2, age, and sex; but now we will approach the problem in a different way, viz. by means of a verbal interference paradigm. Using this, we will attempt to measure the amount of influence that the Swedish past tense formation system exercises in the processing of English present and past tense verbs.

To make the results of the present investigation optimally comparable with those of the preceding noun

test, we strove to parallel the designs and procedures
of the two experiments as far as possible and appropriate.
This means that, first, we collected as stimuli a body
of English verbs which were completely crossed over four
variables[45] – viz. tense, verb inflection, inflection of
and lexical similarity to the Swedish translation equivalent – to create a stimulus matrix where the degree of
theoretical processing difficulty – i.e. the probability
of cross-language interference – differed systematically
over the cells. Second, we employed the same test
population as in the previous experiment, divided into
the same age/English proficiency groups. Third, we used
the same two-choice identification task as before.
Subjects were required to identify as fast and accurately
as possible the tense (present or past) of a series of
successively presented English verbs by pressing one of
two response buttons. Both latencies and errors were
recorded during this performance, parameters which
constituted our dependent measures in the postexperimental analyses. (For a further description of the
stimuli and the method, see p. 151 ff.; for a similar
description of the subjects, see p. 32 ff.)

5.1. Hypotheses

With this sketch of the experimental design in mind,
then, what results can we expect from the verb test?
But before we try to answer that question, it might

---

45. The difference concerning the number of variables
employed in the noun and verb tests – three versus four –
was due to the noun paradigm being curtailed. For ideal
parallelism, complete inflectional crossing – i.e. four
variables – was desired in both stimulus matrices, but
as only a few appropriate nouns with the zero plural
could be found (e.g. aircraft, sheep, and trout; cf.
note 39), we had to exclude the variable plural form
in the noun test.

be appropriate to briefly explain how the Swedish and
English past tense formation systems are structured, since
this will be a central point in the following. (We will
henceforth use the term _past tense_ in the sense of the
preterite only.)

Swedish and English use roughly the same type of system
of past tense inflection. This consists of either a
regular dental suffix, as in English _asked_ and Swedish
frågade, _köpte_, or an irregular marker such as ablaut
or zero past, as in English _bound_, _put_ and Swedish
sprang. (Note that this distinction is not equivalent
to that of weak and strong inflection.) The distribution
of regular and irregular markers is often parallel over
the languages, but not always. There are thus pairs of
translation equivalents that exhibit similar inflection,
e.g. _bake_ - _baked_ vs. _baka_ - _bakade_, as well as such that
show dissimilar inflection, e.g. _float_ - _floated_ vs.
flyta - _flöt_.

If this variation of inflectional congruence is
systematically manipulated and combined with the distinction of cross-language lexical similarity, we achieve a
corresponding interference paradigm to that of the
preceding noun test. The only vital difference is that
another type of stimuli is involved now. This parallelism
enables us to make in principle the same predictions
about the outcome of the two tests. Therefore, with the
proviso that we are concerned with verbs instead of nouns,
we will simply draw on the hypotheses, including their
underlying rationales, of the noun test in formulating
our expectations of the present experiment (cf. p. 122 ff.).
(No attention is paid to the _results_ of that test at this
stage.) The current hypotheses thus read as follows.

Hypothesis I: Incongruent inflections between English
verbs and their Swedish translation equivalents will
engender more interference than congruent inflections.

Hypothesis II: The effect of the inflectional relation
between the languages will be a function of lexical
similarity in such a way that the greatest amount of
interference occurs when the verbs and their translation
equivalents are lexically similar but inflectionally

dissimilar, and the least amount when they are both
lexically and inflectionally similar. Lexically dissimilar verbs will fall in-between these, with incongruent
inflections yielding more interference than congruent also
in this category.

Hypothesis III: The degree of interference between the
Swedish and English past tense formation systems will
decrease with increasing age/English proficiency level
in our subjects.

Hypothesis IV: There will be no essential difference
between the amounts of interference that males and females
exhibit.

5.2. Description

Stimuli: Four independent binary variables were
combined to produce a 2 x 2 x 2 x 2 design with 16
different experimental conditions. The variables were
(1) tense (present vs. past, e.g. ask vs. asked), (2) verb
inflection (regular vs. irregular, e.g. talk – talked vs.
hang – hung), (3) inflection of the Swedish translation
equivalent (regular vs. irregular, e.g. spela – spelade
(play – played) vs. ge – gav (give – gave)), and (4)
lexical similarity to the Swedish translation equivalent
(similar vs. dissimilar, e.g. see – se vs. make – göra).
The resulting 16-cell matrix was filled with 80 English
verbs, all of which were considered as having natural and
easily evoked Swedish translation equivalents, yielding
five verbs in each cell (see Figure 25 and Appendix).

The classification of the verbs in terms of lexical
similarity was, as before, carried out on the basis of
writing similarities between the languages, and each
verb was arbitrarily judged by the experimenter to be
either similar or dissimilar to its translation equivalent. Their frequency of use was further checked in
the Kučera & Francis (1967) count and all appeared
relatively common. The factor of stimulus length held
a roughly similar value over the different cells and

the only appreciable difference was observed between
present and past tense verbs (mean lengths = 4.3 and 5.3
letters respectively). The verbs were exposed in white
uppercase letters on a dark background, with each letter
measuring 1.0 cm in height and .5 cm in width.

Figure 25

The stimulus matrix used in the tense choice test.

	similar present	dissimilar present	similar past	dissimilar past
Eng. regular Swe. regular	1A hate (hatar)	1B love (älskar)	1C landed (landade)	1D played (spelade)
Eng. regular Swe. irregular	2A float (flyter)	2B boast (skryter)	2C died (dog)	2D walked (gick)
Eng. irregular Swe. regular	3A ring (ringer)	3B grind (maler)	3C shook (skakade)	3D began (började)
Eng. irregular Swe. irregular	4A drink (dricker)	4B write (skriver)	4C found (fann)	4D knew (visste)

Apparatus: The same equipment and experimental
arrangements as in the previous test on nouns were used.
The only difference was that the response buttons were
labelled present and past respectively this time, and
the signs marking their left-right orientation were
accordingly changed.

Procedure: The testing procedure was similar to that
of the preceding experiment, except that it involved
verbs instead of nouns now. The subjects thus received
the following instructions orally in Swedish. "The test
you are about to take part in is an attempt to investigate
how English verbs are processed in the brain of native
Swedish speakers. You will see the verbs one at a time
on the screen in front of you, and your task is to
decide as quickly as possible whether they are in the
present or in the past tense. If a verb is in the present
tense, press the button marked present; if a verb is in
the past tense, press the button marked past. Your
decisions must be fast and accurate, and if you don't
know which response is the correct one, guess. No feedback

about the correctness of your responses will be given
during the test, and no opportunity to change any of
them is offered."

5.3. Results

The experimental results were analyzed in three
different ways, viz. cell-difference computations on
both latencies and error data, and a correlation test
between these two parameters. Each approach will be
dealt with separately below.

Latencies: The latency data from the present experiment
is summarized in Table 13.

Table 13

Mean latencies (msec) in each experimental condition
and on each value of the within-subject variables in the
verb test.

	Group A			Group B			Group C			
	M	F	Tot.	M	F	Tot.	M	F	Tot.	Total
cell 1A	1298	1261	1280	960	1320	1140	774	768	771	1064
cell 2A	1299	1553	1426	1149	1361	1255	829	828	828	1170
cell 3A	1399	1422	1410	1024	1250	1137	850	814	832	1126
cell 4A	1090	972	1031	789	994	891	700	740	720	881
cell 1B	1155	1133	1144	836	1005	920	770	733	751	939
cell 2B	1352	1433	1393	1017	1277	1147	763	771	767	1102
cell 3B	1316	1222	1269	1154	1254	1204	786	865	826	1099
cell 4B	1161	1288	1225	1030	1115	1073	829	791	810	1036
cell 1C	929	816	873	771	827	799	687	688	688	786
cell 2C	924	924	924	759	860	809	715	689	702	812
cell 3C	1321	1363	1342	988	1315	1151	839	867	853	1115
cell 4C	1316	1435	1375	1010	1218	1114	863	816	840	1110
cell 1D	917	826	872	708	796	752	714	683	698	774
cell 2D	935	897	916	758	837	797	711	751	731	815
cell 3D	1280	1329	1304	1024	1416	1220	816	809	813	1112
cell 4D	1241	1335	1288	960	1092	1026	822	793	808	1041

(Continued on the next page.)

Table 13 (continued)

	Group A			Group B			Group C			
	M	F	Tot.	M	F	Tot.	M	F	Tot.	Total
present	1259	1286	1272	995	1197	1096	788	789	788	1052
past	1108	1116	1112	872	1045	959	771	762	766	946
Eng. reg.	1101	1106	1103	869	1035	952	745	739	742	933
Eng. irreg.	1266	1296	1281	997	1207	1102	813	812	813	1065
Swe. reg.	1202	1172	1187	933	1148	1040	780	778	779	1002
Swe. irreg.	1165	1230	1197	934	1094	1014	779	772	775	996
similar	1197	1218	1208	931	1143	1037	782	776	779	1008
dissimilar	1170	1183	1176	936	1099	1017	776	774	775	990
Total	1183	1201	1192	933	1121	1027	779	775	777	999

M = males, F = females

In the following figures, the gist of the latency data
in Table 13 is reproduced graphically.

Figure 26

Mean latencies for present and past tense verbs as
a function of age/English proficiency level in the verb
test.

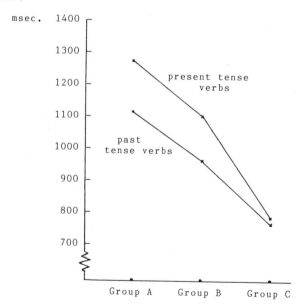

Figure 27

Mean latencies for regular and irregular verbs as
a function of age/English proficiency level in the verb
test.

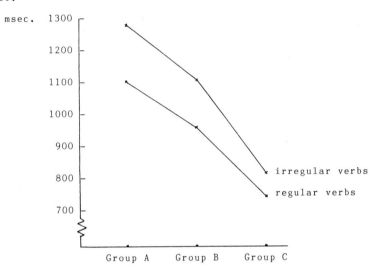

Figure 28

Mean latencies for verbs with regular and irregular
Swedish translation equivalents as a function of age/
English proficiency level in the verb test.

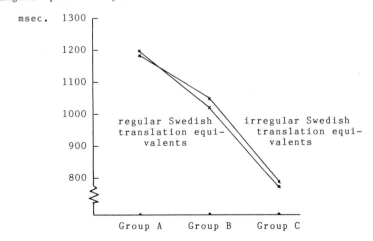

<u>Figure 29</u>

Mean latencies for verbs with lexically similar and
dissimilar Swedish translation equivalents as a function
of age/English proficiency level in the verb test.

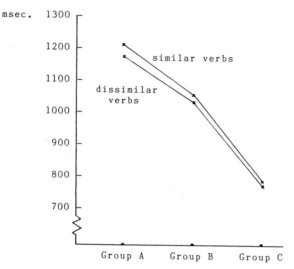

<u>Figure 30</u>

Mean latencies for males and females as a function of
age/English proficiency level in the verb test.

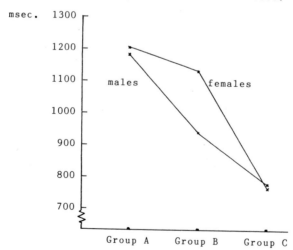

Figure 31

Mean latencies for the three age/English proficiency
groups as a function of experimental condition in the
verb test.

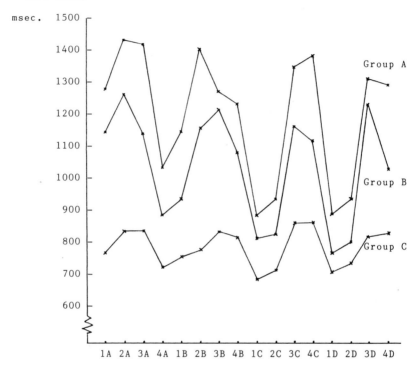

As can be seen, the present experiment produced patterns
similar to those of the preceding test on nouns. The curves
again display an approximate parallelism over the different
values of the variables and there is an even more marked
decrease of latency from Group A to Group C. The greatest
separation appears to exist within the variables of tense,
verb inflection, and age/English proficiency level, while
the curves for Swedish inflection and lexical similarity
more or less coincide. The only irregular relation is
found within the variable of sex, where a small difference
in Group A develops into a large one in Group B and ends
up in a reversed state in Group C.

A six-way analysis of variance with repeated measures, involving age/English proficiency level (3) and sex (2) as between-subject variables and tense (2), verb inflection (2), inflection of the Swedish translation equivalent (2), and lexical similarity to the Swedish translation equivalent (2) as within-subject variables, was performed on the material to test the reliability of the observed trends. The following three significant main effects emerged.

Age/English proficiency level. The latencies declined with increasing age/proficiency level, i.e. Group A had the longest mean response time (1192 msec), Group B was intermediate (1027 msec), and Group C had the shortest mean response time (777 msec), ($F(2,54)=12.9$, $p<.01$). Tense. Past tense verbs were identified faster than present tense verbs (mean latencies = 946 vs. 1052 msec), ($F(1,54)=35.5$, $p<.01$). Verb inflection. Verbs with regular inflection produced shorter latencies than verbs with irregular inflection (mean latencies = 933 vs. 1065 msec), ($F(1,54)=95.6$, $p<.01$).

There were no significant effects from inflection of the Swedish translation equivalent (mean latencies = 1002 vs. 996 msec), cross-language lexical similarity (mean latencies = 1008 vs. 990 msec), and sex (mean latencies = 965 vs. 1032 msec).

Moreover, there emerged no less than 17 significant interactions. Tense x age/English proficiency level. The latency difference between present and past tense verbs decreased with increasing age/proficiency level, i.e. Group A had a mean difference of 160 msec, Group B 137 msec, and Group C 22 msec, ($F(2,54)=5.8$, $p<.01$). Verb inflection x age/English proficiency level. The latency difference between regular and irregular verbs decreased with increasing age/proficiency level, i.e. Group A had a mean difference of 178 msec, Group B 150 msec, and Group C 71 msec, ($F(2,54)=5.6$, $p<.01$). Tense x verb inflection. Irregular verbs gave shorter latencies in the present tense than in the past (1036 vs. 1094), whereas regular verbs gave shorter latencies in the past tense than in the present

(796 vs. 1069 msec), (F(1,54)=76.8, p<.01). <u>Verb inflection x lexical similarity to the Swedish translation
equivalent</u>. The latency difference between regular and
irregular verbs was greater when the verbs were lexically
dissimilar than when they were similar (mean differences =
165 vs. 100 msec), (F(1,54)=8.1, p<.01). <u>Verb inflection x
inflection of the Swedish translation equivalent</u>. Congruent
past tense inflection between English and Swedish resulted
in shorter latencies than incongruent inflection, irrespective of type of inflection on the stimulus verb. Among
the regular verbs, the regular(regular) condition was
faster than the regular(irregular) condition (mean
difference = 84 msec) and among the irregular verbs,
the irregular(irregular) condition was faster than the
irregular(regular) condition (mean difference = 96 msec),
(F(1,54)=56.3, p<.01). <u>Inflection of the Swedish translation equivalent x lexical similarity to the Swedish
translation equivalent</u>. Lexical similarity between the
languages tended to favour verbs with irregular inflection
on the Swedish equivalents (mean latencies = 993 msec
(irregular) vs. 1023 msec (regular)), while the reverse
was true for dissimilarity, verbs with regular inflection
on the Swedish equivalents being responded to faster
(mean latencies = 981 msec (regular) vs. 998 msec (irregular)), (F(1,54)=5.7, p<.05).

The tense x verb inflection interaction (see above)
proved to be a productive base for further, more complex
interactions. <u>Tense x verb inflection x age/English
proficiency level</u>. The relation between tense and verb
inflection was dependent on level of age/proficiency.
In Groups A and B, irregular present tense verbs were
identified faster than regular ones (mean differences =
77 msec (A) and 39 msec (B)), whereas regular past tense
verbs were identified faster than irregular ones (mean
differences = 431 msec (A) and 338 msec (B)). In Group C,
regular verbs resulted in shorter latencies than irregular
irrespective of tense (mean differences = 18 msec in the
present tense and 124 msec in the past tense), (F(2,54)=
9.9, p<.01). <u>Tense x verb inflection x sex</u>. Females
produced greater latency differences between regular and

irregular verbs in the present and past tense respectively (mean differences = 60 vs. 350 msec) than did males (mean differences = 6 vs. 250 msec), (F(1,54)=4.3, p<.05). Tense x verb inflection x lexical similarity to the Swedish translation equivalent. In the present tense, similar regular verbs were identified faster than irregular ones (mean difference = 113 msec), while dissimilar verbs displayed the opposite pattern, with irregular verbs being the fastest (mean difference = 47 msec). In the past tense, irregular verbs took longer time than regular ones irrespective of value on the similarity variable (mean differences = 313 msec (similar) and 282 msec (dissimilar)), (F(1,54)=15.8, p<.01). Tense x verb inflection x inflection of the Swedish translation equivalent. There were greater differences between congruent and incongruent inflection across language for both regular and irregular verbs in the present tense condition (mean differences = 135 msec (regular) and 154 msec (irregular)) than in the past tense condition (mean differences = 33 msec (regular) and 38 msec (irregular)), (F(1,54)=20.3, p<.01).

In addition, there were two four-way interactions qualifying the above tense x verb inflection interaction further. We will not however comment on these, since they are too complex to allow of a reliable interpretation, but just list them and give their level of confidence. Tense x verb inflection x inflection of the Swedish translation equivalent x age/English proficiency level, (F(2,54)=3.2, p<.05). Tense x verb inflection x lexical similarity to the Swedish translation equivalent x inflection of the Swedish translation equivalent, (F(1,54)= 7.8, p<.01).

Moreover, the lexical similarity to the Swedish translation equivalent x inflection of the Swedish translation equivalent interaction (see above) was further restricted in a three-way and a five-way interaction. Lexical similarity to the Swedish translation equivalent x inflection of the Swedish translation equivalent x tense. The relation between lexical similarity and Swedish inflection varied with tense of the verbs. The difference

between similar and dissimilar regular translation equivalents was greater than for similar and dissimilar
irregular ones in the present tense (mean differences =
76 msec (regular) and 45 msec (irregular)), whereas the
reverse relation applied to the past tense condition
(mean differences = 7 msec (regular) and 33 msec (irregular)), $(F(1,54)=14.0, p<.01)$. Lexical similarity
to the Swedish translation equivalent x inflection of
the Swedish translation equivalent x verb inflection x
age/English proficiency level x sex. (No interpretation
is attempted here because of the high complexity level of
the interaction.) $(F(2,54)=3.5, p<.05.)$

The verb inflection x age/English proficiency level
interaction (see above) was also qualified further in
two three-way interactions. Verb inflection x age/English
proficiency level x lexical similarity to the Swedish
translation equivalent. The latency differences between
regular and irregular verbs in relation to lexical
similarity varied with level of age/proficiency. Similar
regular and irregular verbs and dissimilar regular and
irregular ones diverged most respectively in Group B
(mean difference = 155 msec), while these divergencies
were quite small in Group A and Group C (mean differences =
26 msec and 13 msec respectively), $(F(2,54)=3.9, p<.05)$.
Verb inflection x age/English proficiency level x inflection of the Swedish translation equivalent. The latency
differences between congruent and incongruent inflection
over language varied with age/proficiency level. Whereas
the differences were relatively great in Group A and
Group B (mean differences = 112 msec and 126 msec respectively), the difference in Group C was quite small (mean
difference = 33 msec), $(F(2,54)=5.7, p<.01)$.

Finally, there was also an inflection of the Swedish
translation equivalent x age/English proficiency level x
sex interaction. The latency difference between the values
on the Swedish inflection variable depended on type of
subject. The differences between regular and irregular
inflection of the translation equivalent diverged most
between males and females in Group B (mean difference =
53 msec), while the corresponding divergencies in Groups

A and C were found to be only 21 msec and 6 msec respectively, (females exhibited a smaller mean difference than males in each of the three groups), $(F(2,54)=3.9,$ $p<.05)$.

Errors: The error data from the present experiment is summarized in Table 14.

Table 14

Mean error rate (%) in each experimental condition and on each value of the within-subject variables in the verb test.

	Group A			Group B			Group C			
	M	F	Tot.	M	F	Tot.	M	F	Tot.	Total
cell 1A	16.0	6.0	11.0	14.0	12.0	13.0	4.0	8.0	6.0	10.0
cell 2A	18.0	14.0	16.0	20.0	22.0	21.0	8.0	4.0	6.0	14.3
cell 3A	20.0	10.0	15.0	18.0	8.0	13.0	4.0	12.0	8.0	12.0
cell 4A	2.0	6.0	4.0	4.0	6.0	5.0	2.0	2.0	2.0	3.7
cell 1B	4.0	0	2.0	2.0	2.0	2.0	0	0	0	1.3
cell 2B	12.0	10.0	11.0	12.0	8.0	10.0	4.0	4.0	4.0	8.3
cell 3B	28.0	8.0	18.0	20.0	18.0	19.0	4.0	6.0	5.0	14.0
cell 4B	12.0	4.0	8.0	6.0	2.0	4.0	4.0	2.0	3.0	5.0
cell 1C	0	0	0	0	2.0	1.0	2.0	2.0	2.0	1.0
cell 2C	2.0	0	1.0	0	2.0	1.0	0	0	0	.7
cell 3C	22.0	22.0	22.0	20.0	14.0	17.0	14.0	10.0	12.0	17.0
cell 4C	28.0	30.0	29.0	14.0	16.0	15.0	8.0	12.0	10.0	18.0
cell 1D	0	0	0	4.0	0	2.0	2.0	0	1.0	1.0
cell 2D	4.0	0	2.0	0	0	0	0	2.0	1.0	1.0
cell 3D	36.0	32.0	34.0	14.0	16.0	15.0	14.0	10.0	12.0	20.3
cell 4D	32.0	36.0	34.0	16.0	20.0	18.0	6.0	8.0	7.0	19.7
present	14.0	7.3	10.6	12.0	9.8	10.9	3.8	4.8	4.3	8.6
past	15.5	15.0	15.3	8.5	8.8	8.6	5.7	5.5	5.6	9.8
Eng. reg.	7.0	3.8	5.4	6.5	6.0	6.3	2.5	2.5	2.5	4.7
Eng. irreg.	22.5	18.5	20.5	14.0	12.5	13.3	7.0	7.8	7.4	13.7
Swe. reg.	15.8	9.8	12.8	11.5	9.0	10.3	5.5	6.0	5.8	9.6
Swe. irreg.	13.8	12.5	13.1	9.0	9.5	9.3	4.0	4.3	4.1	8.8
similar	13.5	11.0	12.3	11.3	10.3	10.8	5.3	6.3	5.8	9.6
dissimilar	16.0	11.2	13.6	9.3	8.3	8.8	4.3	4.0	4.1	8.8
Total	14.8	11.1	12.9	10.3	9.3	9.8	4.7	5.1	4.9	9.2

M = males, F = females

Figure 32

Mean error rates for present and past tense verbs as a
function of age/English proficiency level in the verb test.

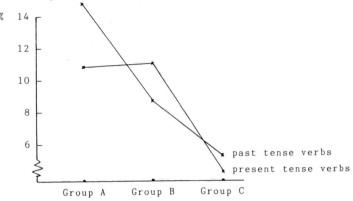

Figure 33

Mean error rates for regular and irregular verbs as a
function of age/English proficiency level in the verb test.

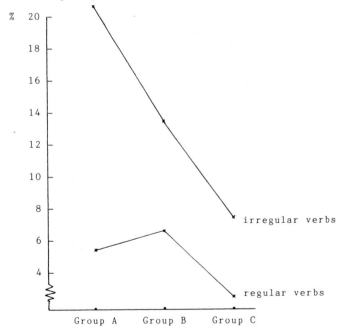

Figure 34

Mean error rates for verbs with regular and irregular
inflections on their Swedish translation equivalents as
a function of age/English proficiency level in the verb test.

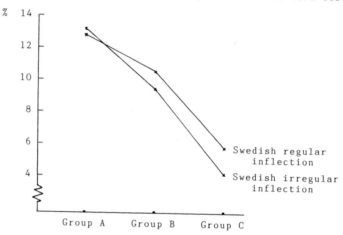

Figure 35

Mean error rates for verbs with lexically similar and
dissimilar Swedish translation equivalents as a function
of age/English proficiency level in the verb test.

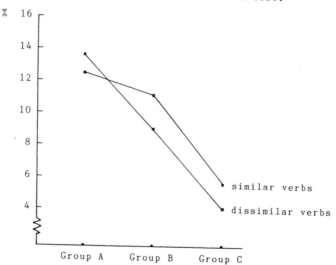

Figure 36

Mean error rates for males and females as a function of age/English proficiency level in the verb test.

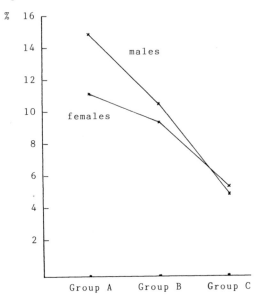

From the graphic transformations of the main data in Table 14, we can see that the error measure gave slightly more complex and interwoven patterns than the previous latency measure (cf. p. 129 ff.). Five out of six graphs contain disordinal curves and the sixth (verb inflection), on the contrary, shows a substantial separation. The overall impression from the latency analysis remains, however – a rough parallelism between the curves still exists and there is a clear decrease of error rate with increasing age/English proficiency level.

The statistical treatment of the error data consisted of a six-way analysis of variance with repeated measures involving the same variables as the latency analysis. Two significant main effects emerged. Age/English proficiency level. The error rate diminished with increasing age/English proficiency level, i.e. Group A had a mean error rate of 12.9%, Group B 9.8%, and Group C 4.9%,

Figure 37

Mean error rates for the three age/English proficiency
groups as a function of experimental condition in the
verb test.

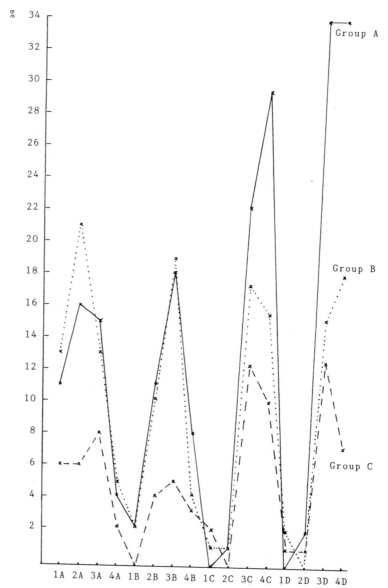

(F(2,54)=16.3, p<.01). <u>Verb inflection</u>. Regular verbs
caused fewer errors than irregular verbs (mean error
rates = 4.7% vs. 13.7%), (F(1,54)=76.4, p<.01).

There obtained no significant effects of tense (mean
error rates = 8.6% and 9.8%), inflection of the Swedish
translation equivalent (mean error rates = 9.6% and 8.8%),
cross-language lexical similarity (mean error rates =
9.6% and 8.8%), and sex (mean error rates = 9.9% and
8.5%).

Furthermore, 10 significant interactions emerged.
<u>Tense x age/English proficiency level</u>. The error rate
difference between present and past tense verbs declined
with increasing age/proficiency level, i.e. Group A had a
mean difference of 4.4%, Group B 2.1%, and Group C 1.4%,
(F(2,54)=4.5, p<.05). <u>Verb inflection x age/English
proficiency level</u>. There was a decline of the error rate
difference between regular and irregular verbs with
increasing age/proficiency level, i.e. Group A had a mean
difference of 15.1%, Group B 6.5%, and Group C 4.1%,
(F(2,54)=9.2, p<.01). <u>Tense x verb inflection</u>. Whereas
the error rates for regular and irregular verbs were
similar in the present tense (8.5% and 8.7% respectively),
they differed considerably in the past tense (.9% and
18.2% respectively), (F(1,54)=76.6, p<.01). <u>Tense x
lexical similarity to the Swedish translation equivalent</u>.
In the present tense, lexically similar verbs engendered
more errors than dissimilar ones (mean error rates =
10.0% vs. 7.2%). In the past tense, the pattern was
reversed, with dissimilar verbs yielding more errors
than similar ones (mean error rates = 10.5% vs. 9.2%),
(F(1,54)=6.4, p<.05). <u>Verb inflection x lexical similarity
to the Swedish translation equivalent</u>. The error rate
difference between regular and irregular verbs was
greater among the lexically dissimilar verbs than among
the similar ones (mean differences = 11.9% vs. 6.2%),
(F(1,54)=10.2, p<.01). <u>Verb inflection x inflection of
the Swedish translation equivalent</u>. Verbs with congruent
inflection across language generated fewer errors than
those with incongruent inflection. In other words, the
regular(irregular) condition produced more errors than

the regular(regular) one (mean error rates = 6.1% vs. 3.3%) and the irregular(regular) condition similarly caused more errors than the irregular(irregular) one (mean error rates = 15.8% vs. 11.6%), (F(1,54)=26.6, p<.01). Tense x verb inflection x age/English proficiency level. While the error rate difference between regular and irregular verbs was negligible in each of the three age/English proficiency groups in the present tense (mean differences = 1.3% (A), 1.2% (B), and .5% (C)), the corresponding differences varied considerably with age/proficiency in the past tense (mean differences = 29.0% (A), 15.3% (B), and 9.3% (C)). In all conditions, except the present tense for Group B, the regular verbs gave lower error rates than the irregular ones. (F(2,54)= 7.4, p<.01.) Tense x verb inflection x lexical similarity to the Swedish translation equivalent. In the present tense, similar regular verbs produced more errors than similar irregular ones (mean error rates = 12.2% vs. 7.8%), whereas dissimilar irregular verbs yielded more errors than dissimilar regular ones (mean error rates = 9.5% vs. 4.8%). In the past tense, irregular verbs led to more errors irrespective of value on the similarity variable (mean error rates = .8% and 17.5% (similar) and 1.0% and 20.0% (dissimilar)), (F(1,54)=4.3, p<.05). Tense x verb inflection x inflection of the Swedish translation equivalent. The difference between verbs with congruent and incongruent inflection across language was dependent on tense. The pattern seen in the two-way interaction verb inflection x inflection of the Swedish translation equivalent (see above) was valid for verbs in the present tense only, i.e. that congruence of verb inflection yielded fewer errors than incongruence (mean error rates = 5.7% (regular(regular)), 11.3% (regular(irregular)), 13.0% (irregular(regular)), and 4.3% (irregular(irregular))). In the past tense, irregular verbs produced a substantially higher error rate than regular ones irrespective of Swedish inflection (mean error rates = 1.0% (regular (regular)), .8% (regular(irregular)), 18.7% (irregular (regular)), and 18.8% (irregular(irregular))), (F(1,54)= 18.4, p<.01). Tense x inflection of the Swedish transla-

tion equivalent x age/English proficiency level x sex.
(No comment is made here because of the high complexity
level of the interaction.) (F(2,54)=3.5, p<.05.)

Latencies - errors: Analogically with the noun test,
a correlation test (Fischer's Z-method) was carried out
between our two dependent measures - latency and error
rate. Again, the intention was to find out whether or
not these potential parameters of stimulus difficulty
reflected to any appreciable extent the same properties
of verbal identification, in particular interference.
The overall condition, i.e. where the three age/English
proficiency groups were taken together, gave a non-
significant Z=.17, indicating that there was a general,
but moderate tendency for the error rate to increase
when the latencies increased, or conversely, for the
error rate to decrease when the latencies decreased.
When a Z-value was calculated for each of the three
subject groups, the following figures evolved. Group A =
.19, Group B = .26, and Group C = .06, (F(2,56)=7.3,
p<.01).[46] Hence, the correlation latency-error rate
seems to be dependent on age/English proficiency level,
since the groups differed significantly on the value of
the Z-coefficient. The lower levels, Groups A and B,
displayed a relatively strong covariation between the
parameters, while a similar trend was only barely
visible at the highest level, Group C.

5.4. Discussion

As we can see, the present experiment produced a
multitude of statistically significant effects. In
particular, there is a large number of complex interactions, the occurrence of which might appear surprising

---

46. One subject (Group C) identified all the verbs
correctly (error rate = 0%), and had therefore to be
excluded from this analysis.

since they are not paralleled in the noun test. However,
there seem to be two logical reasons for this proliferation.
On the one hand, the present test obviously offered a
wider range of processing difficulty than the preceding
and thereby occasioned greater performance differences
over the different experimental conditions (see Tables 13
and 14; cf. Tables 11 and 12). On the other hand, due to
the addition of yet another stimulus variable, the verb
matrix was double the size of the noun matrix (16-cell
versus 8-cell designs), which means that there were
twice as many responses to base the statistical analyses
on here. From statistical theory, we know that given a
constant performance difference, the likelihood of it
reaching significance increases with the number of
observations used in the calculations (e.g. Keppel, 1973).

Below, we will try to evaluate the working hypotheses
of the present experiment. As before, this treatment
will be divided into within-subject and between-subject
considerations, also including some comments on other
interesting performance differences that are not directly
related to any of the hypotheses. (For reasons of space
and interpretability of the data, we will not however
bring up for discussion all of the demonstrated effects.)

Within-subject effects: The most intriguing effects
that obtained within the stimulus matrix were verb
inflection x inflection of the Swedish translation equivalent (latencies) and verb inflection x inflection of
the Swedish translation equivalent (errors). As explained
before, these interactions indicate that verbs with
incongruent inflection over language took longer time to
respond to and caused more errors respectively as
compared to congruent verbs.[47] The combined force of

---

47. The effects of inflectional congruence-incongruence
were apparently also a function of tense in the sense that
present tense verbs engendered greater performance differences than past tense verbs. See the interactions tense x
verb inflection x inflection of the Swedish translation
equivalent (latencies and errors), p. 160 and p. 168.

these effects, each of which was among the strongest that
occurred over each performance parameter, argues for the
tense of the incongruent stimuli being harder to identify
than that of the congruent. The most plausible explanation
of this difference seems to be that in the processing of
the incongruent verbs, but not the congruent, the Swedish
inflectional system interfered with the English to some
extent, thereby delaying subjects' responses and making
them less accurate. This means that the predicted interference effect between verb inflections stated in Hypothesis I is confirmed by both the latency and error data,
and also that the corresponding single interference effect
(latencies) in the noun test now takes on more respectability. Thus, in other words, the general implication of
Hypothesis I - i.e. that there exist inflectional cross-
cueing between Swedish and English - appears to be verified.

Hypothesis II, in contrast, was not endorsed by our
experimental findings. Contrary to expectations, neither
latencies nor error distribution yielded any indications
in favour of the theory that inflectional interference
is a function of lexical similarity, i.e. that the amount
of interference would diminish gradually over the conditions lexical similarity/inflectional dissimilarity -
lexical and inflectional dissimilarity - lexical dis-
similarity/inflectional similarity - lexical and inflectional similarity. The data rather indicate that the
lexical and inflectional variables were independent of
each other as possible cross-language cues in subjects'
execution of the test task. Clearly, this result makes
heavy inroads into our original processing theory, and
since a similar state of affairs was suggested in the noun
test, it accordingly seems as if Hypothesis II is not
valid in either of our experimental contexts.

Further, we may note the effects of <u>verb inflection</u>
(latencies) and <u>verb inflection</u> (errors). These show
that regular verbs were in general responded to both
faster and more accurately than irregular verbs, and
that subjects thus found it easier to identify the tense
of this material. The explanation of this effect is
probably related to the differential application of

past tense markers in the two categories of stimuli.
Since regular verbs by definition always indicate the
past tense by means of the suffixes -d or -ed, and since
normally no such suffixes, nor any similar systematicity,
are present in irregular verbs (as the name of the
category implies), subjects may have responded past
mechanically each time a stimulus carried a dental suffix.
If this is so, a possibility which has been noted by
Clark & Clark (1977), the speed and accuracy of the
responses given to past tense regular verbs would by this
strategy have been considerably improved in relation to
the responses given to other types of stimuli, and as a
consequence the whole class of regular verbs (of which
the past tense forms constitute half) would on the
average appear to have been easier to process than that
of the irregular verbs. The credibility of this argument
is supported by the interactions tense x verb inflection
(latencies) and tense x verb inflection (errors), in
which the main operative factors unmistakably were the
markedly low latencies and error rate produced by the
past tense regular verbs (cf. p. 158 and p. 167).

Related to the above -(e)d-strategy is apparently
also the effect of tense (latencies). This indicates
that past tense verbs were identified significantly
faster than present tense verbs, and this despite the
fact that the former were on the average one letter
longer and probably also less frequent than the latter
(inflected forms generally are, e.g. MacKay, 1976).
Most likely, the cause of this effect is the proposed
facilitated identification of the past tense verbs
carrying a dental suffix, the result of which would be
that the mean latency for the whole category of past
tense verbs fell below that of present tense verbs.

Perhaps this effect was amplified to some extent by
a presumably inhibitory morphological non-correspondence
in the present tense, where the (hypothetical) Swedish
words, but not the English (no third person singular
forms were used), carried a suffix, for example as in
kallar from kalla versus call from call. This also seems
to mean that the -(e)d-strategy, with the possible aid

of the suffixal incongruence in the present tense,
exerted much more influence upon subjects' responses
than the factors of word-length and word-frequency
together.

   Between-subject effects: Concerning performance
differences across individuals, the effect of verb
inflection x inflection of the Swedish translation
equivalent x age/English proficiency level (latencies)
is momentous. This interaction shows that subjects in
Groups A and B produced significantly slower responses
to verbs with incongruent inflection in relation to
their Swedish equivalents than to verbs exhibiting
inflectional congruence, whereas only a small corresponding
difference occurred in Group C. In accordance with
previous reasoning, the most tenable explanation of this
effect seems to be that in the processing of the incongruent verbs, subjects in the lower and middle range
of age/English proficiency experienced a greater amount
of response-delaying interference from the Swedish
inflectional system than those in the upper range of
this parameter. From this, the earlier base effect of
interference (verb inflection x inflection of the
Swedish translation equivalent - latencies) may be
specified to have emanated primarily from the performance
of Groups A and B. The present findings thus confirm the
prediction of Hypothesis III that the degree of interference between the Swedish and English past tense
formation systems would decrease with increasing
age/English proficiency level. Since this outcome is
in agreement with that of the noun test, it now also
seems justified to accept the notion that inflectional
interference, irrespective of type, is a function of
age/English proficiency level.
   No important differences over sex were found. Males
and females seem on the whole to have performed about
equally in carrying out the test task. The only
(interpretable) exceptions to this parallelism were,
on the one hand, a tense x verb inflection x sex (latencies) interaction, signifying a tendency for females to

produce greater latency differences than males between
regular and irregular verbs in both the present and the
past tense, and, on the other hand, a moderate speed-
for-accuracy tradeoff, showing that whereas males made
faster responses to the stimuli, females were more
accurate in identifying the tense of them (see Figures
30 and 36; cf. the noun test, in which a similar trend
obtained). However, as there apparently was no crucial
difference in the amount of inflectional interference
that males and females experienced, the prediction of
Hypothesis IV that sex would be irrelevant to this type
of interference is borne out by the test results. This
means that the present data align with the findings of
the noun test also regarding sex.

Further, we may notice that subjects' overall performance was a function of age/English proficiency level,
as expected. The older and more proficient the subjects,
the faster and more accurate they were in identifying
the tense of the verbs (age/English proficiency level
(latencies) and age/English proficiency level (errors);
see Figures 31 and 37). This development is also mirrored
in the interactions tense x age/English proficiency level
(latencies) and tense x age/English proficiency level
(errors), and verb inflection x age/English proficiency
level (latencies) and verb inflection x age/English
proficiency level (errors), which indicate that both
speed and accuracy differences between present and past
tense verbs and regular and irregular verbs respectively
diminished with increasing age/English proficiency level
(see Figures 26 and 32, and Figures 27 and 33). These
declining trends thus imply that the overall processing
difficulty in the test, as well as the differences of
this factor across tense and verb inflection, were felt
most strongly in Group A, less in Group B, and least in
Group C. (For a tentative explanation of the above
effects, see the corresponding section of the noun test,
p. 145).

Lastly, we may also call attention to the fact that
no significant correlation between latencies and error
rates occurred in the data. Although the present results,

in contrast to the noun test, indicate a marginal covariation between these parameters (Z=.17), this is
clearly not what we expected a priori, since both
measures were used with the intention that they should
reflect variations in stimulus difficulty similarly.

However, as proposed in the discussion of the preceding experiment (pp. 146-147), latencies and errors
are obviously coupled to partly distinct aspects of the
processing difficulty that the present task presented.
Whereas the error distribution seems to be related to
a large extent to subjects' potential unfamiliarity
with the stimuli, or to procedural problems of responding,
the latency data, which is more subtle, probably go
deeper into subjects' performance, mirroring also such
effects that were caused by cross-language interference.
This would then explain why there were more effects of
latencies than of errors in the "interference-loaded"
conditions in each of our two experiments.

6. General discussion

Having evaluated the separate results of the noun
and verb tests, it is now time to try to integrate
the combined implications of these findings into a
model of neuropsychological function. To do this conveniently, the ensuing discussion will employ two
different perspectives of organization, viz. interlingual and intergroup relations.

Interlingual relations: As we have seen, the anticipated
occurrence of cross-language inflectional interference
was demonstrated in both our experiments. If these
effects are real, as we believe they are, they indicate
that the Swedish inflectional system interfered somewhat
with the English in subjects' processing of the stimuli
when they were incongruent and thus went in different
directions, whether nouns or verbs. Logically, this seems
to mean that the two inflectional systems were somehow

connected with each other, and that the underlying
Swedish and English morphological representations, of
which the inflectional systems constitute major components, were interdependent to some extent in the brain
of our subjects (cf. Lambert, 1969).

If we compare this conclusion with previous findings
and claims about morphological organization in bilinguals,
however, we find that they are not particularly consonant.
As stated before (p. 109), earlier studies have typically
indicated that inflectional interference is a rare
phenomenon, which occurs in exceptional cases of bilingual
performance only. Such observations have led scholars to
propose that the morphological systems in the brain are
in principle independent (e.g. Albert & Obler, 1978).
In contrast to this stand the present findings, which
imply a greater extent of interrelatedness, since the
recorded interference, though subtle, obviously was of
a general character, constituting the rule rather than
the exception in subjects' response data.

The key to this seemingly paradoxical state is however
not difficult to find. First, we may note that two
different kinds of verbal performance are involved.
In previous studies, the attention has been directed
almost exclusively to aspects of language production
(e.g. Weinreich, 1953; Vildomec, 1963), while our
experiments have dealt with reception. As we know from
both clinical and experimental work (see p. 104 and pp.
107-108), the language-specific expressive abilities in
bilinguals tend to be more independent than corresponding
receptive ones, and the corollary of this is then that
there should occur less interference in production than
in reception.

Second, the divergence over modality is probably
amplified by the distinct measures of interference
applied. Earlier studies have been largely confined to
observations of inflectional transfer across language
(e.g. Weinreich, 1953; Duškova, 1969), a measure which
in its binary character and singularity seems too gross
to give an accurate picture of the often delicate effects
of interference. The likely outcome of such investigations

is therefore that the amount of inflectional interference is underestimated. Our experimental method, in
contrast, is not affected by this problem. By using two
complementary measures, i.e. one quasi-continuous
(latency) and one binary (error rate), we presumably
cover the whole range of potential interference, from
outright confusion effects generating errors (which would
be on roughly the same gross level as transfer in production) down to minute distraction effects inhibiting
subjects' responses marginally only. It stands to reason
that this approach is more sensitive to the occurrence
of inflectional interference, and thereby also arguably
gives clearer evidence of the extent to which the morphological systems are neuropsychologically connected.

Third, the differential findings may be due to the
fact that we employed a bilingual population that was
more liable than bilinguals in general to produce interlingual interference. This would be so because they were
subsidiary bilinguals, whom we have defined as persons
who have learnt L2 in a primarily formal manner at
school, with extended associations between L1 and L2
being built up during this type of linguistic contact.
Such a manner of acquisition should have augmented
rather than diminished the degree of interdependence
between the languages, and for this reason enhanced the
possibility of interference between them as well.

Hence, we may infer that the difference between the
results of the present experiments and those of previous
studies constitutes no real contradiction, but is rather
a logical product of the differential objectives and
methods employed. This view clearly accentuates the
need for researchers to distinguish between output and
input interference in language performance, as well as
to be on the alert regarding the consequences of different
types of test population and investigation technique.
It also establishes that our demonstrated effects of
receptive interference may be accepted without any
necessary qualifications from earlier studies on
expressive interference.

Thus, from what has been said hitherto, it seems as

if the morphological systems in our subjects are interdependent to the extent that they are capable of producing
a significant amount of inflectional interference in
input processing. If we delve deeper into this matter,
we may now ask ourselves what factors govern this
functional organization and how their influence is
exercised.

A priori, we stated our expectation that lexical
similarity across language would be a relevant factor
in this context. In particular, we claimed that in
addition to the general trend for semantically similar
words to activate each other (conceptual similarity),
the test stimuli would be more likely to prime their
Swedish translation equivalents if they were lexically
similar than if they were dissimilar, and that this
difference would have repercussions on how much inflectional interference there occurred. The underlying
assumption of this proposal was that the lexical form of
a word and its pertinent inflection would be so closely
connected in the brain that if the word was activated
through cross-language priming, the inflectional information would be triggered too. Theoretically, this implies
that in those cases where the stimuli primed their
Swedish equivalents maximally - i.e. through both
conceptual and lexical similarity - but where the inflections did not correspond over language, there would
occur a considerable amount of inflectional interference,
because the simultaneously (though not equally) activated
English and Swedish inflectional systems would yield
conflicting information.

On the other hand, if only conceptual, but not lexical,
priming obtained, as would be the case with lexically
dissimilar material, the interference effect would be
weaker, because the Swedish inflectional system would
be less alerted and therefore not capable of interfering
with the English to the same extent. (We may leave the
conditions with congruent inflections aside here.)

As we have seen, however, no interaction between
inflectional interference and lexical similarity
obtained in either of our experiments. Contrary to the

above theory, the lexically similar and dissimilar
stimuli engendered about equal amounts of interference
in our subjects, a finding which implies that no lexical
priming took place, i.e. that the factor of lexical
similarity was largely inoperative over the different
inflectional conditions.

There are on the face of it two ways of explaining
this unexpected outcome. On the one hand, it may
constitute an experimental artifact, the occurrence
of which can never be ruled out altogether in investigations of the present type. If this is the case, the true
effect of lexical similarity might have been obscured
by biased stimulus sampling, inappropriate test measures,
or even a generally defective test procedure. This
solution does not seem very likely, though, since apart
from the fact that the applied stimulus paradigms were
carefully composed and the investigation methods strictly
controlled, the non-effect of lexical similarity was a
general finding obtaining in two independent experiments.

On the other hand, the present results may be due to
the factor of lexical similarity not being strong enough
to influence subjects' performance significantly. The
reason for this may be that the effects of semantic
priming that occurred were so much stronger that they
overshadowed or suppressed those of lexical similarity,
meaning that the recorded inflectional interference
was conditioned exclusively, or at least principally,
by conceptual similarity between the stimuli and their
Swedish equivalents. Such similarity is of course not
absolute, since there are often different shades of
meaning between translations, but the semantic correspondence is approximate only. Yet it is obviously
sufficient to generate notable priming effects (e.g.
Kolers & Gonzalez, 1980).

Indeed, there are three different arguments that
bolster up this view. First, the approximately constant
amount of interference that obtained over the stimuli
seems more compatible with a constant determinative
factor than with a variable one. The factor of conceptual
similarity was constant in our material, as this involved

(presumed) pairs of translation equivalents only, while
the factor of lexical similarity was binary, assuming
either the value similar or dissimilar. Second, previous
studies have shown that no interference occurs between
languages if no semantic processing takes place (e.g.
Kintsch & Kintsch, 1969). Third, as the semantic systems
in bilinguals are thought to be more interdependent[48]
than the lexical (e.g. Albert & Obler, 1978), it seems
more likely that the channel of cross-language priming
is established at this level.

Evidently, each of these arguments favours the notion
that the factor of conceptual similarity was pre-eminent
above that of lexical similarity as the decisive coding
parameter in our subjects. It thus seems justified to
regard the proposed priming effect across language as
contingent essentially upon Swedish-English conceptual
similarity, and that the occurrences of inflectional
interference accordingly was a function of this factor.

On the basis of this conclusion, we may sketch a
tentative model of subjects' processing in carrying out
the test tasks as follows. When a stimulus was presented,
two cognitive processes were triggered. On the one hand,
the English lexical and morphological systems were
activated for analysis of the incoming information,
and on the other, there occurred a more or less automatic
transformation of the stimulus into its underlying
semantic concept (cf. e.g. Lambert & Preston, 1967).
While lexicomorphemic comparisons with the pertinent
material stored in memory commenced at the surface level
in order to determine the form of the stimulus - i.e.
singular versus plural or present versus past - a
priming effect took place at the deep level, where the
Swedish translation equivalent was activated through the
common semantic representation of this word and the

---

48. Some researchers have in fact suggested that bilinguals possess a common semantic system for their
languages (e.g. Glanzer & Duarte, 1971; Lopez & Young,
1974). If this is true, it would only make our theory
of semantic priming look even more plausible.

stimulus. This process led to the translation equivalent
becoming a sort of "secondary" stimulus, and as a consequence the Swedish lexical and morphological systems
were alerted as well (semi-activated). In other words,
the stage was set for interlingual processing interference to occur at the surface level, and this without
any effect of lexical priming as originally proposed.

When a decision was to be made as to the form of
the stimulus, the lexicomorphemic comparisons within
the English systems were interfered with by intruding
Swedish material. As long as the information corresponded
over language, or non-correspondences were confined to
the lexical domain, the identification process was not
measurably disturbed, but when there were conflicting
inflectional (morphological) properties, such items
being subjects' target information, a notable delay
and perhaps an erroneous decision was the result. This
degeneration in performance was directly reflected in
the responses subsequently given, constituting, as
already explained, our interference effects.

Only when obvious structural cues were present, as
in stimuli carrying -(e)s or -(e)d suffixes, did pure
surface strategies take precedence over this processing
pattern. In such cases, the salient inflectional endings
indicated the correct response directly, before any
cross-language priming and potential interference
effects had obtained. (However, these strategies did
not change the relative amounts of interference in
lexically similar and dissimilar material, since both
types of stimuli were equally affected by them.)

The above cognitive model is of course only hypothetical, since we cannot conclusively establish its
validity. Nevertheless, as it dovetails with our experimental findings as well as being in agreement with
previous major theoretical constructs such as the
concept mediation hypothesis (e.g. Potter et al., 1984;
Kroll & Potter, 1984), we will keep to it here and use
it as a basis for further conclusions.

This acceptance is not uncontroversial, though.
One problem, for example, is our rejection of lexical

similarity as a cross-language priming factor. Whereas
previous studies on receptive interference - for example
bilingual Stroop tests (e.g. Preston & Lambert, 1969;
Dyer, 1973) - have yielded support for a marked influence
from this factor, no such effects were demonstrated in
our experiments. It is hard to procure a ready-made
solution to this divergence, but probably the differential
scopes characterizing these investigations bear the brunt
of it. Previous studies have generally focused on lexical
interference, while our tests pertain to morphological
interference, with all the differences of material and
methodology that this distinction entails. Without
engaging too much in speculation, we may say that the
treatment of the lexical similarity factor in the two
approaches seems rather different, this factor constituting the primary interference parameter in one type
of study and a subordinate stimulus parameter in the
other, and it is thus not wholly unexpected that it
should appear to play somewhat different roles in such
distinct settings. This is however not the same as
saying that differences of lexical priming necessarily
were to be expected.

Leaving that as it may be, we may in short establish
that the putative partly interdependent state of the
morphological systems in our subjects seems to be
conditioned principally by conceptual, and not lexical,
similarities between Swedish and English. Let us now
turn from the within-subject perspective of our findings
to between-subject considerations. What factors can we
find in this realm that qualify the exhibited occurrences
of morphological interference?

Intergroup relations: To start with, we may recollect
that the hypothesized interaction between inflectional
interference and age/English proficiency level obtained
in both our experiments. As pointed out before, these
effects indicate that the extent of interference decreased
with increasing age/proficiency level, meaning that the
youngest and least proficient subjects of Group A
exhibited the greatest amount of interference, those of

Group B were intermediate, and the oldest and most proficient subjects of Group C exhibited the least amount. If these data are construed in terms of a functional relationship between the language-specific morphological systems in the brain, we may claim that our beginner-learners were more interdependent (or less independent) than the more advanced learners, and that this difference was the result of a gradual development from a relatively interdependent to a more independent type of language organization with increasing age/English proficiency level. This conclusion seems quite plausible on its own account, and even more so in the light of previous studies - as we remember from Section 3, eight out of 11 investigations on this issue lent support to the notion that a similar compound-to-coordinate transition with increasing L2-proficiency (and probably age too) occurs generally in most bilinguals. It is thus fairly certain that the effect of age/English proficiency level in our material is a real one, and accordingly that this factor is a significant conditioner of the functional relation between the morphological systems in our subjects.

But why, then, should differences in age/English proficiency appear to influence the way in which bilinguals process language in the brain? Extended knowledge of a language or a higher age of its user does not per se require any changes in the interlingual relationship, but might just as well establish more firmly a once developed organizational state.

To find a tenable explanation for this effect, we may for a moment hark back to the concluding discussion of Chapter II (p. 86 ff.). Here, we argued that the recorded differences of cerebral lateralization over the three subject groups were due primarily to partly differential processing strategies in carrying out the test tasks. Specifically, the subjects in the lower range of age/English proficiency were seen to be using a deeper or more semantic mode of linguistic analysis than those in the upper range, who rather seemed to apply a more superficial approach, involving mainly structural

properties of the stimuli. This divergence was explained
in terms of the different types and degrees of language
experience and cognitive ability that our subjects are
thought to represent, thus indicating that the shift of
processing strategies was correlated with the value of
the age/English proficiency factor.

If we draw on the claims of this discussion, we may
explain the present interference findings in a similar
way. Let us first assume that the distinction between
deep and superficial processing over low- and high-
proficient subjects is valid here too. This would mean
that the subjects of Group A used primarily semantic
processing in identifying the form of the stimuli, i.e.
they tended to extract the meaning of each word before
analyzing its form; those of Group B utilized semantic
and structural processing more equally; those of Group C
used structural processing predominantly, i.e. they
drew on surface attributes of the stimuli as far as
possible, without any unnecessary semantic analyses
(cf. Craik & Lockhart, 1972; Cermak & Craik, 1979).
Each of these strategies would be feasible in order to
perform successfully, since theoretically both semantic
and structural characteristics may be used as primary cues
to determine the number or tense of the stimuli (cf. for
example the word girls, the number of which may be
identified either by producing, for instance, a mental
image of two girls, or by using directly the cue that
the final s constitutes).[49]

It is likely that these divergent approaches have
different potentials for generating inflectional interference. Recalling that our interference effects appeared
to be incited principally by conceptual, and not lexical,

---

49. Admittedly, a mental image of a past tense verb is
somewhat more difficult to conceive of than one of a
plural noun. (Uninflected forms seem to pose much less
of a problem in this respect.) One way to generate such
a concept might be to project internally the action
reflected by the verb in question, plus a time axis or
a similar device showing "pastness".

similarity between the stimuli and their translation
equivalents - i.e. by semantic rather than structural
properties - a neat link may be established between
the demonstrated decline of interference over age/English
proficiency level and subjects' putative modes of processing. Ratiocinating briefly, if the amount of interference is dependent upon semantic similarities across
language, and semantic analysis is emphasized in one type
of processing but de-emphasized in another in favour of
structural concern, there would surely occur more interference in the former approach than in the latter. This
would be so because semantic, but not structural,
analysis necessarily activates the underlying concepts
of words (e.g. Kintsch, 1977), which, as we have seen,
obviously constitute the main cross-language priming
mechanism in our subjects. The fact that Group A
exhibited the greatest amount of interference, Group B
was intermediate, and Group C showed the least amount,
may thus be explained by the above proposed decreasing
reliance on semantic processing with increasing age/Eng-
lish proficiency level.

   This explanation requires of course that we are able
to substantiate that a certain semantic-to-structural
processing transition actually occurred across our
subjects. Such evidence is however not particularly
difficult to find. First, we have the findings from the
preceding lateralization experiments, in which there
were several indications supporting a development from
deep to superficial processing over age/English proficiency level (p. 86 ff.). As we are concerned with
the same subjects and a partly similar test design -
i.e. a lexical stimulus-response task - now, it seems
quite probable that a similar processing pattern is valid
in the present context as well.

   Second, the fact that subjects performed faster (and
more accurately) the older and more proficient they were
(age/English proficiency level - latencies, in both tests)
implies that they experienced the difficulty of the
tasks somewhat differently and used different approaches
in executing them. Although a certain portion of this

effect must be attributed to the different degrees of
language experience, it also seems to be a function of
processing strategy. Presumably, the subjects of Group A
were slowest in responding not only because they were
the least proficient, but also because they carried out
time-consuming semantic transformations of the stimuli[50]
before analyzing the form of them, which seems to be
too lengthy and laborious a mode of processing here,
since in fact no (absolute) understanding of the material
was necessary in order to perform successfully. The
subjects of Group B and in particular those of Group C,
on the other hand, responded faster not only because
they were more proficient, but probably also because
they managed to set aside semantic properties to
different extents and instead focus on superficial,
structural cues of the stimuli. Judging from our test
data, such a strategy is both swifter and more expedient
in identifying the form of the presented items, since
it apparently involves fewer task-irrelevant mental
operations. (Cf. the significant latency-error rate
correlation differences across age/English proficiency
level (p. 141 and p. 169), which also imply that subjects
went about the test tasks somewhat differently.)

Third, structural-semantic processing distinctions
have been indicated in subsidiary bilinguals before.
Kintsch & Kintsch (1969), for example, using the terms
primary (structural) and secondary memory processing
(semantic), showed that when their subjects employed
structural processing, no cross-language interference
occurred, but when they used semantic strategies, it
did (the languages were German and English). Although
no age/proficiency factor was reported here, these
findings seem quite compatible with our own theory of
differential processing.

The cause of the hypothesized shift in processing

---

50. That semantic transformations take time in receptive
language processing has been empirically demonstrated
by, for example, Pellegrino et al. (1977) and Potter &
Faulconer (1975).

strategies appears, as already discussed in Chapter II,
to lie in subjects' different linguistic and cognitive
abilities. Regarding the influence of language competence,
the three different levels of English proficiency
represented seem to be correlated with similar differences
in reading experience (cf. Macnamara, 1970), and in
particular so as the subjects apparently have acquired
English primarily through a passive, visual mode. This
means that subjects would have been more familiar with
visual English stimuli - i.e. the material used in our
experiments - the more proficient they were. It is
probable that the amount of such familiarity is related
to the type of processing strategy applied in carrying
out the test tasks. If so, subjects with a low degree
of language exposure would be less apt than more advanced
ones to perform the presumed task-optimal, structurally-
based type of analysis, since their linguistic data base
was not as yet adequately developed to meet the requirements of this approach, with semi-automatic identification
of a wide range of words and their possible inflections.
This deficiency, whatever its extent, would instead have
to be made up for proportionally by semantic processing,
which apparently was both less efficient and more
cumbersome. We may thus say that the amount of language
exposure was negatively correlated with semantic processing, meaning that the more experienced subjects
were in reading, the more superficially they tended to
analyze the test stimuli. This effect would then also
be tied to subjects' differential dependence on the
languages in general, as proposed earlier (pp. 84-85).

In the case of cognitive status, the factors of age
and intellectual capacity seem to be relevant. On the
one hand, the advance of age over the three test groups
implies that there was a concomitant increase in
cognitive maturation, or in other words, that subjects
became more able to process language abstractly and
metalinguistically the older they were. On the other
hand, the putative similar rise of intellectual capacity
suggests that subjects were "smarter" the older and more
proficient they were, the result of which would be that

they possessed a greater repertoire of processing
strategies that were applied in accordance with the
principle of maximal efficiency and parsimony (cf. p.
91). Since the structurally-based mode of analysis
presumably requires a great deal of both abstraction
ability and dynamic strategy application, it is likely
that this approach was reserved for the older and more
proficient subjects who were in command of these cognitive
abilities. The less advanced subjects, in contrast,
probably had to rely relatively more on the less
demanding, but more awkward and redundant semantic type
of processing due to their hypothesized lower level of
cognitive sophistication. This reasoning thus implies
that cognitive ability too was important for how subjects
carried out the test tasks, and in particular, that the
higher the level of this ability was, the more structural,
or less semantic, was the stimulus analysis performed.

Concisely put, then, we contend that the inferred
shift from an interdependent to a more independent type
of morphological functional organization in the brain
of our subjects seems to be conditioned primarily by
divergent processing strategies in dealing with the
stimuli. These strategies would derive from subjects'
differential linguistic and cognitive abilities as
represented by their distinct levels of age/English
proficiency. Thus, in other words, it seems as if the
suggested compound-to-coordinate transition is not
primarily, if at all, a question of a neurophysiological
change with increasing age/English proficiency level,
but rather of a shift in cognitive mode over this factor.
If so, subjects' cognitive approach to word processing
would vary with linguistic experience, biological
maturation, and mental predisposition, while their
underlying functional organization of the cerebral
substrate would remain roughly constant (at least there
is no convincing evidence for a difference). This hypothesis accordingly implies that the language-specific
morphological representations of the substrate in our
subjects in fact bore a similar mutual relation in each
of the three test groups - i.e. they were constantly

predominantly independent, but yet interdependent to the
extent that subtle cross-language inflectional interference could occur in receptive, but presumably not in
productive, processing.

Finally, a few words may also be said about sex in
this context. As we have seen, neither the noun nor the
verb test yielded any significant differences of inflectional interference over this factor, but males and
females turned out to be about equally sensitive to
influence from their native language in identifying the
form of the stimuli. This outcome is what we expected,
since the evidence gleaned from previous work on this
issue suggested that there are no crucial sex differences
in the underlying neuropsychological organization of the
languages (pp. 113-115). (For recent findings in terms of
neuroanatomical sex differences in general, however,
see Kimura, 1983.)

As the previous group differences of interference
were defined as being caused chiefly by divergent modes
of processing, the lack of such effects here implies
that no essential differences in terms of cognitive
approach (nor of neurophysiological deployment of course)
occurred over sex. In other words, males and females
appear to have used similar processing strategies on
the average, with equal degrees of depth (semantic
reliance) or superficiality (structural reliance) in
carrying out their stimulus analyses. The only exception
to this equivalence seems to be the demonstrated speed-
for-accuracy tradeoffs (in both experiments), which
indicate that males were faster but females more
accurate in responding to the presented words. Evidently,
however, this difference did not affect the dependence
relation between the languages, since no uneven
distribution of interference across sex was observed.
Thus, we may establish that sex, in contrast to
age/English proficiency level, does not seem to be
a relevant factor in the functional organization of the
morphological systems in our subjects.

Summary: Epitomizing the present chapter, then, we

may make the following claims.

(1) The morphological representations in the brain of
our Swedish-English subsidiary bilinguals seem to be
interdependent to the extent that significant interlingual interference may occur in receptive verbal
performance. The previous theory of a near-total independence of these systems, based mainly on studies of
language production, apparently needs a revision,
therefore, to account for the present findings.

(2) The demonstrated interference effects do not
appear to be conditioned by lexical phonetic-graphic
similarity between Swedish and English as first thought,
but rather almost exclusively by conceptual similarity.
This implies that cross-language priming occurs primarily
at the semantic level.

(3) The amount of interference tended to decrease
with increasing age/English proficiency level in our
subjects. This trend presumably derives from divergent
processing strategies in carrying out the test tasks,
which in their turn would originate from subjects'
different levels of linguistic and cognitive ability.

(4) Males and females seem to be equal regarding
their functional organization of the morphological
systems.

IV. Conclusion

As a final step in this thesis, let us now try to
crystallize the implications of the present investigation by juxtaposing and evaluating the main strands of
evidence brought forward in the preceding lateralization
and interdependence experiments. Our aim here is not
only to achieve a compendious account of the ultimate
test results, but also to disclose any parallel trends
within these data which might serve to identify possible
general principles concerning the broad neuropsychological
organization of language in the bilingual population
tested.

In the introductory chapter, we posed three focal
questions about how language is represented in the
bilingual brain. These questions, which have constituted
the guideline of our experimentation, were in turn:
What types of lateralization and interdependence patterns
would the test group exhibit? What factors would condition
or influence these patterns? What would variation in
these patterns consist of - neurophysiological or
psychological change? Hopefully, on the basis of our
combined findings, we will now be able to supply, or
at least suggest, some of the overall answers to these
questions, however tentative and speculative they might
be.

Starting with the patterns of organization, we may
establish that two prevailing types - one localizational
and one functional - emerged. In the former case, a
clear left-hemisphere dominance obtained for the processing of both Swedish and English lexical stimuli,
and in the latter, there was a significant processing
interconnection between the morphological elements of
these languages. Although a great deal of variation
occurred within these patterns, there being important
performance differences both within and between subjects,
the overall profile is clearly that of a basic interlingual parallelism and integration in the data. The
cause of these results is most likely that the underlying representation of the languages was deployed in

a corresponding, parallel manner, where the language-
specific systems at each linguistic level engaged
essentially common or intermixed processing mechanisms
respectively. In other words, inasmuch as it is possible
to generalize from lexical and morphological data, there
is good reason to believe that the languages were on
the whole organized in a mutually similar fashion in
the brain, both in terms of localization and function.

If this conclusion is compared with previous studies
on language organization in bilinguals, we find ample
evidence to support it. The most weighty findings come
from clinical investigations - as we have seen, a large
majority of bilinguals tend to suffer parallel impairment
and/or restitution of their languages in case of damage
to the language-relevant areas in the brain. If the
ability to use one language is disturbed, that of the
other is as a rule affected similarly (see Section 1 in
Chapters II and III). This makes a cogent argument in
favour of shared or integrated linguistic organization,
and then not only in aphasic patients, but also in
non-damaged bilinguals, since it is not likely that a
sudden transition from an unparallel to a parallel state
occurs when a person becomes aphasic.

In experimental studies, corresponding organizational
indications have been found. Although the variability
has been higher in this type of data, there is a number
of psycholinguistic tests in which similar lateralization
patterns, extensive interlingual interference, or other
notable connections between the languages have obtained
(see Section 2 in Chapters II and III). These findings,
which basically espouse those from the clinical domain,
thus further substantiate our case for a fundamentally
uniform organization.

In addition, there are two (and perhaps more) logical
considerations that might be brought to bear on this
issue. First, we may observe that there exist certain
verbal processes that seem to have a unique representation
in the brain. Two such examples are articulatory
programming and acoustic comprehension, which are
thought to be subserved primarily by structures in and

around Broca's area (in the frontal lobe) and Wernicke's
area (in the temporal lobe) respectively, both situated
in the left hemisphere (e.g. Luria, 1970). For the
bilingual, who strives to achieve efficient performance
in both his languages, it is necessary to have each
language system intimately connected to – and therefore
arguably closely organized around – these common functions.
The most plausible way to fulfil this requirement appears
to be to establish a parallel or integrated type of
language organization. (Cf. Whitaker (1978) who claimed
that "it is almost certain that all languages are
represented and organized similarly in the same anatomical
structures" (p. 28).)

Second, the way in which English was acquired seems
to be of relevance. Since our subjects already knew a
great deal of Swedish when they commenced learning this
language, it is probable that they utilized their previous
linguistic competence to some extent when internalizing
the English material. This would be so in particular as
the learning took place in a school setting for the main
part, where formal study and interlingual comparison
tend to be major ingredients, and also because the
languages were structurally similar, with the high level
of cross-language compatibility that this entails.
Presumably, these learning conditions promoted a rather
close association between the Swedish and English verbal
systems, the likely consequence of which is that the
underlying language correlates in the brain became
considerably integrated. This means, in other words,
that we are faced with yet another indication in favour
of a basically compound language organization in our
subjects.

Evidently, then, a fundamentally uniform representation
of language is highly probable. Still, this is apparently
only part of the explanation as to why our patterns of
organization came out as they did. As we remember, there
was a significant variation in the extent to which our
subjects evinced left-hemisphere lateralization for
and interdependence between the processing of the
languages. These differences indicate that on top of

the postulated uniform language base, there was another
organizational component that was individually variable
and therefore able to cause divergences in subject
performance. The main purpose of the elaborate para-
metrical analyses carried out in each of our experiments
has been to identify the different constituents of this
component by means of finding innate or developmental
characteristics in the individual that might have
conditioned these. Let us now synthesize the results
from these to see what we eventually came up with.

In the pre-experimental background surveys (Section 3
in Chapters II and III), we reviewed work carried out
on or pertaining to 11 factors that might be relevant to
how bilinguals organize their languages in the brain.
Of these, we chose seven for further investigation
either in terms of localizational or functional influence,
or both, viz. the innate sex and familial handedness and
the developmental-environmental age, manner and age of
language acquisition, language proficiency, and interlingual structural similarity. It was however not
possible to analyze all of these factors separately,
as we have seen, since some of them were nested within
each other, but we had to form the compounds age/English
proficiency level and language (including age and manner
of acquisition). These fusions thus left us with five
variables appropriate for statistical analyses.

The test results showed that three of these variables
covaried with processing differences in our subjects.
There were significant effects of language, structural
similarity, and age/English proficiency level, while no
weighty influence was recorded from sex and familial
handedness. Though these findings did not align with
previous research in all instances, they seem to make
sense in the limited context of language material and
test population that we have been concerned with. (We
must not forget that experimental design and approach
are quite important factors in studies within the
neuropsychological domain; cf. p. 92 ff.) Since we have
already discussed the organizational implications of
each recorded effect (or non-effect) in its separate

framework (Section 6.2 in Chapter II and Section 6 in
Chapter III), we shall here merely bring together the
different conclusions arrived at.

First, then, we have got the effect of language
(tested in terms of lateralization only). This indicates
that there were differences in how Swedish and English
words were treated in the brain, and in particular that
the former type of material engaged relatively more of
left-hemisphere processing mechanisms than the latter.
The root of this divergence is presumably to be found
within the different contexts in which the languages
were learnt. Whereas our subjects acquired their mother
tongue, Swedish, in infancy and childhood using an
informal, communicational method primarily, the learning
of English did not commence until the age of 10 and then
in a more formal, metalinguistic manner. The differences
of age and mode of acquisition imply, on the one hand,
that the languages were internalized at two distinct
levels of biological and cognitive maturation in the
brain, and, on the other, that rather different cognitive
strategies were employed on these occasions. As shown
before (p. 79 ff.), it is probable that this gave rise
to a certain processing distinction between the languages,
where Swedish words were treated in a relatively deep or
semantic mode and English words in a somewhat more
superficial or structural manner. Since previous
research has indicated that the left cerebral hemisphere
is more adept at semantic processing and the right at
structural-holistic processing, we seem to have reached
a tenable explanation as to why the Swedish words
appeared more left-lateralized in the brain than the
English.

Second, there was an effect of interlingual structural
similarity (tested in terms of interdependence only).
English words with incongruent, but not congruent,
inflection in relation to their Swedish translation
equivalents generated notable processing interference
in our subjects. The implication of this finding is that
the underlying morphological systems must have been
considerably connected across language, as there occurred

inhibition between them. No special explanation was
needed here, however, since this interdependent state
of organization is well in accordance with what has been
said before about language in the bilingual brain - i.e.
that there is a general tendency towards uniform or
integral deployment. We may only add that the degree of
morphological interconnection probably was enhanced by
the applied learning strategies - i.e. the formal type
of study where the foreign language is often associated
or compared with the native language - and by the rather
close grammatical correspondences that exist between
Swedish and English.

Third, we recorded an effect of age/English proficiency
level (tested in terms of both lateralization and interdependence) which was perhaps the most important and
interesting finding in our analyses. This indicates
that subject processing patterns varied in such a way
that the extent of both left-lateralization of the
languages and interlingual dependence decreased with
increasing age/English proficiency level. Presumably,
the source of this development lies in subjects'
different cognitive and linguistic abilities in relation
to the demands of the experimental tasks. Since the
rising value of the age/proficiency factor seems to have
entailed, on the one hand, a greater cognitive maturation
and intellectual capacity, and, on the other, a broader
linguistic knowledge and experience, it is likely that
these differences in their turn had repercussions on
how the verbal material was treated in the brain.
As shown earlier (p. 86 ff. and p. 182 ff.), there is
considerable evidence to the effect that young and
low-proficient subjects - i.e. those who possessed a
rather limited cognitive and linguistic repertoire -
used a fairly deep, semantic strategy when processing
language, and that this mode of analysis was gradually
replaced by a more superficial, structural approach
when they became older and more proficient - i.e. when
they achieved a higher degree of cognitive and linguistic
sophistication.[51] This strategic transition may be neatly
coupled with the demonstrated decline of both left-

hemisphere reliance and interlingual dependence. In the
former case, we are faced with the same effect as for
the previous language factor, viz. that left-lateralization
diminished as right-hemisphere-specialized structural
processing was substituted to some extent for left-
hemisphere-specialized semantic processing. In the latter
case, the effect seems to be due to the cross-language
connections, which apparently consist of semantic
associations primarily, becoming less activated and
therefore less influential as subjects' processing
strategies changed from a basically semantic type to
a more structural one.

Fourth, there was no effect of subject sex (tested
in terms of both lateralization and interdependence).
This means that males and females exhibited approximately
equal degrees of both left-hemisphere language dominance
and interlingual dependence. On the basis of this and
the fact that there was no essential difference in
cognitive or linguistic status between the sexes, there

---

51. An appropriate way of evaluating our structural-
semantic processing distinction further might be to
give subjects an ad hoc memory test unexpectedly after
each experiment. This would show which subjects remembered
the stimulus words best, and since retention in memory
seems to be dependent primarily on semantic analysis
(e.g. Kintsch, 1977), it would also indicate which
subjects relied most on semantic processing. An alternative procedure (in the lateralization tests only) is to
show subjects pictures or other conceptual representations of the stimuli postexperimentally and ask them to
supply the language in which each item was presented.
The subjects who remembered the language-specific forms
best would also reasonably be those who were most inclined
to structural processing, since language-tagging is a
typical aspect of structural analysis (cf. Rose et al.,
1975). No memory tests of this type were however performed
as we have seen (they were not part of the original
project, simply). Instead, we suggest this approach as
a matter for future research.

is no reason to believe anything but that they processed
verbal material in a similar manner and with equal proportions of semantic and structural analysis.

Fifth, finally, there was no effect of familial
handedness either (tested in terms of lateralization
only). Though a caveat should be entered here as to the
reliability of this outcome (see p. 97 ff.), it implies
as it stands that there was no crucial difference between
the degrees of left-hemisphere language specialization
that subjects with and without familial left-handers
displayed. Apparently, then, we have got a parallel case
to that of sex here - the two target groups seem to have
possessed a uniform neuropsychological organization of
language and therefore used a similar mode of processing
when dealing with the test material.

From the above findings, we can see that there
occurred two factor effects which gainsay the previous
claim of a uniform language base in our subjects, viz.
the processing differences across language and age/Eng-
lish proficiency level. (The effect of structural
similarity only indicates that there was a considerable
amount of interconnection between the languages.) This
suggests that the principal source of variation in our
lateralization and interdependence patterns was harboured
within these factors, and in particular, as both the
language and the age/English proficiency effect
apparently were due to differences in age and manner
of language acquisition and/or in cognitive maturation
and potential, that this consisted of different levels
of cognitive and linguistic ability and experience in
the test population. In other words, when subjects'
performance diverged from each other in any of the
experimental tasks, it was most likely not caused by
any change in the neural substrate, but rather by
differentially applied processing modes or strategies
conditioned by individual differences in cognitive-
linguistic status.

If we now return to the issue of what the recorded
language patterns actually measured, it is probable that
two different organizational components were involved.

On the one hand, there is the neurophysiological component, which seems to be reflected in the basic parallelism and integration in the test data. As touched on earlier, this would consist of genetically preprogrammed structures in the brain which are reserved for language functions already at birth (cf. Geschwind & Levitsky, 1968). It is this substrate that houses the total body of verbal information acquired, whether one, two, or more languages, and it is this substrate that is affected when a person becomes aphasic. Its localization is variable - we have seen that it tends to be a function of certain innate characteristics, for example subjects' hand preference and perhaps also their familial handedness (although this was not demonstrated in our research), but hardly of sex - but once the genetic determination has been completed, it seems to remain stable and equable (but see note 30). This may be said because no natural (measurable) modification of individuals' neurophysiological organization with developmental changes in language processing has as yet been demonstrated, at least not to our knowledge. The language substrate thus has a static character which is conditioned primarily by hereditary factors and from which, if in sole control, the bilinguals' languages would always appear equally and unalterably lateralized and interdependent, theoretically speaking.

On the other hand, we have the psychological component. It is within this we find the source of our recorded processing variation, since subjects' deduced organizational patterns covaried with differences over the psychological variables cognitive and linguistic ability and experience. This component is viewed as a superordinate layer to that of the neurophysiological, where basic language data and functions are adapted in terms of certain applications or modes of usage, for example structural or semantic processing, to meet the requirements of a specific verbal task as far as possible. Apparently, such adaptation becomes more refined and target-oriented the more mature and experienced an individual is. It is thus this psycho-

logical control system rather than any strict neurophysiological organization that changes with an
individual's linguistic development, and it is therefore
to this dynamic component that our differences in
processing patterns between languages and individuals
respectively should be attributed.[52]

Finally, the above conclusions may also be brought to
bear on neuropsychological language research in general.
Since quite a few scholars within this field seem to
have been too rash to answer or have simply begged the
question of what their experimentally or clinically
derived patterns of language organization and changes
within these consist of (e.g. Albert & Obler, 1978;
Paradis, 1977; Lambert & Fillenbaum, 1959), the present
findings accentuate the need to carefully identify the
basis of any such research results. It is undeniable
that several investigations have, intentionally or not,
yielded the impression that demonstrated organizational
differences have been anatomically or physiologically
founded, and this without any adequate supporting
evidence. To give just one example, Albert & Obler
(1978) in their major study of the bilingual brain
conclude that "the circumstances of the learning may
affect the eventual neural (our emphasis) organization
of that language" (p. 242). As the authors adduce no
specific evidence in favour of any neural, or neurophysiological, changes with progressive language learning,
a more proper term here would be (neuro)psychological
organization, as suggested by our own theory of modi-

---

52. It is probably also within the psychological component
that we find the explanation of "the remarkable ability
of bilinguals to keep their languages apart" (p. 110)
marvelled at by many scholars over the years. As a natural
implication of our theorizing, this vital separation
seems to have a psychological rather than a neurophysiological basis, and consequently theoretical
constructs such as that of a "switch mechanism" (see p.
106 and pp. 110-111) would, if relevant at all, be
established at or pertain to this level of organization.

ficatory processes in the brain.

Statements like this seem to have led to our view of the brain and its linguistic mechanisms becoming somewhat inaccurate or biased at times. What has been purely psychological changes in the individual have somewhat rashly been interpreted in terms of neuro-physiological differentiation. The consequence of this is most likely that a certain underestimation has occurred of the significance of the psychological component in organizational processes of language in general. Hopefully, the present thesis has contributed, however modestly, to put this component in its right perspective.

Summary: In a nutshell, then, the present series of experiments yielded the following findings and conclusions.

(1) Swedish-English subsidiary bilinguals tend to organize their languages in a roughly uniform and integrated manner in the brain. On the one hand, both languages were evidently processed primarily by the left cerebral hemisphere, and, on the other, the languages showed a significant degree of functional interdependence.

(2) When organizational differences occur, they seem to be a function of subjects' age/English proficiency level, age and manner of language acquisition, and cognitive ability.

(3) The organization of language in our bilinguals appears to consist of two different components – a basic neurophysiological substrate and a superordinate psychological processing system. Evidently, the former is conditioned by genetic properties and therefore relatively static once it has been determined, while the latter proved to be a more dynamic system that changes with developmental-environmental influence. It was within this psychological processing component that the source of our recorded organizational variation was to be found.

Appendix

Stimuli used in the auditory and visual lateralization experiments. (In the latter, the words were neither paired in blocks nor divided into instalments as below, but given randomly in six-word blocks only.)

<u>Swedish test</u>

<u>Instalment A</u>	<u>Instalment B</u>	<u>Instalment C</u>
gård - korg	tid - deg	möta - nysa
lat - rät	rusa - leva	val - fot
baka - peta	skev - ljus	låda - röta
fin - våt	duka - tala	gapa - koka
öka - äga	skum - stam	gul - kal
bråk - gris	snål - smal	tom - dum
veta - fara	rät - lat	hel - söt
from - vred	seg - hög	fara - veta
glad - blid	ila - yra	leva - rusa
dra - tro	tiga - dyka	korg - gård
mått - natt	eka - yta	gris - bråk
alm - orm	våt - fin	äga - öka

<u>Instalment D</u>	<u>Instalment E</u>
blid - glad	stam - skum
häst - fisk	nysa - möta
orm - alm	yra - ila
tala - duka	dum - tom
ljus - skev	hög - seg
peta - baka	vred - from
smal - snål	kal - gul
natt - mått	deg - tid
yta - eka	koka - gapa
tro - dra	söt - hel
dyka - tiga	fot - val
röta - låda	fisk - häst

English test

Instalment A	Instalment B	Instalment C
skin – step	kill – give	calm – tame
dark – tall	bed – dog	date – bite
evil – oval	girl – coal	oval – evil
brow – tree	lake – rope	day – toe
rude – loud	comb – gain	sail – fall
gain – comb	base – pale	tall – dark
hang – sing	end – ant	bowl – pile
sore – sure	fat – hot	meet – need
grey – true	arm – owl	talk – dive
pile – bowl	draw – grow	hot – fat
spit – stop	own – eat	loud – rude
dive – talk	thin – full	give – kill

Instalment D	Instalment E
shop – fish	owl – arm
sure – sore	bite – date
deep – cool	full – thin
sing – hang	fall – sail
dog – bed	need – meet
true – grey	grow – draw
tree – brow	tame – calm
stop – spit	pale – base
step – skin	toe – day
ant – end	fish – shop
coal – girl	eat – own
rope – lake	cool – deep

(The five different pseudo-random orders of the
instalments were A-B-C-D-E, B-C-D-E-A, C-D-E-A-B,
D-E-A-B-C, and E-A-B-C-D in both the Swedish and the
English test in the auditory experiment.)

APPENDIX

Stimuli used in the interdependence experiment on nouns.

Cell 1A	Cell 1B	Singular controls	
ring	girl	bus	dress
ball	road	kiss	ass
hat	bed	gas	business
place	chair	class	mess
rose	pig	circus	campus
		glass	surplus
Cell 2A	Cell 2B	cross	fuss
ship	beard	minus	toss
bone	leg	pass	fuss
room	cloud	plus	toss
lion	tool		
tower	crime		

Cell 3A	Cell 3B	Plural controls	
cats	boys	misses	stresses
lamps	spoons	presses	fortresses
cups	birds	bosses	mistresses
films	bells	guesses	asses
cows	fools	rebuses	dresses
		glasses	surpluses
Cell 4A	Cell 4B	crosses	fusses
bands	roofs	minuses	tosses
houses	saints	passes	fusses
eggs	ends	pluses	tosses
loans	jumps		
shots	goals		

Stimuli used in the interdependence experiment on verbs.

Cell 1A	Cell 1B	Cell 1C	Cell 1D
hate	ask	praised	played
bake	love	opened	washed
start	kill	passed	smoked
live	work	landed	boiled
row	paint	waited	hunted

Cell 2A	Cell 2B	Cell 2C	Cell 2D
float	boast	floated	carried
glide	pull	glided	cracked
die	walk	died	sounded
suck	roar	sucked	sneaked
grip	starve	gripped	rubbed

Cell 3A	Cell 3B	Cell 3C	Cell 3D
ring	grind	rang	made
hang	dig	hung	grew
shake	speak	swung	began
weave	shrink	wove	drew
spit	throw	shook	forgot

Cell 4A	Cell 4B	Cell 4C	Cell 4D
drink	write	spun	wrote
see	know	found	became
take	run	froze	knew
fall	become	gave	ran
sit	tear	stole	tore

References

Albert, M. & Obler, L. (1978). The Bilingual Brain. New
   York: Academic Press.

Allén, S. (1970). Frequency Dictionary of Present-Day
   Swedish Based on Newspaper Material. Part I. Stockholm:
   Almquist & Wiksell.

Anisfeld, M., Anisfeld, E. & Semogas, R. (1969). "Cross-
   influence between the phonological systems of Lithuanian-
   English bilinguals." Journal of Verbal Learning and
   Verbal Behavior, 8, 257-261.

Barton, M., Goodglass, H. & Shai, A. (1965). "Differential
   recognition of tachistoscopically presented English
   and Hebrew words in right and left visual fields."
   Perceptual and Motor Skills, 21, 431-437.

Basser, L. (1962). "Hemiplegia of early onset and the
   faculty of speech with special reference to the
   effects of hemispherectomy." Brain, 85, 427-460.

Beardsmore, H. (1974). "Development of the compound-
   coordinate distinction in bilingualism." Lingua, 33,
   123-127.

Bentin, S. (1981). "On the representation of a second
   language in the cerebral hemispheres of right-handed
   people." Neuropsychologia, 19, 599-603.

Bever, T. (1974). "The relation of language development
   to cognitive development." Language and Brain:
   Developmental Aspects. Ed. E. Lenneberg. Jamaica
   Plain, MA.: Neurosciences Research Program Bulletin,
   585-588.

Bever, T. (1975). "Cerebral asymmetries in humans are due
   to the differentiation of two incompatible processes:
   Holistic and analytic." Developmental Psycholinguistics
   and Communication Disorders. Eds. D. Aaronson & R.
   Rieber. New York: Annals of the New York Academy of
   Sciences, 263, 251-262.

Blumstein, S. & Cooper, W. (1974). "Hemispheric processing
   of intonation contours." Cortex, 10, 146-158.

Blumstein, S., Goodglass, H. & Tartter, V. (1975). "The reliability of ear advantage in dichotic listening." Brain and Language, 2, 226-236.

Bocca, E., Calearo, C., Cassinari, V. & Migliavacca, F. (1955). "Testing 'cortical' hearing in temporal lobe tumours." Acta Oto-Laryngologica, 45, 289-304.

Bogen, J. (1969). "The other side of the brain. II. An appositional mind." Bulletin of the Los Angeles Neurological Society, 34, 135-162.

Boller, F., Kim, Y. & Mack, J. (1977). "Auditory comprehension in aphasia." Studies in Neurolinguistics, 3. Eds. H. Whitaker & H. Whitaker. New York: Academic Press, 1-63.

Borod, J. & Goodglass, H. (1980). "Hemispheric specialization and development." Language and Communication in the Elderly: Experimental, Clinical and Therapeutic Issues. Eds. L. Obler & M. Albert. Lexington, MA.: Heath.

Branch, C., Milner, B. & Rasmussen, T. (1964). "Intracarotic sodium amytal for the lateralization of cerebral speech dominance." Journal of Neurosurgery, 21, 399-465.

Broadbent, D. (1954). "The role of auditory localization in attention and memory span." Journal of Experimental Psychology, 47, 191-196.

Bryden, M. (1960). "Tachistoscopic recognition of non-alphabetical material." Canadian Journal of Psychology, 14, 78-86.

Bryden, M. (1965). "Tachistoscopic recognition, handedness, and cerebral dominance." Neuropsychologia, 3, 1-8.

Bryden, M. (1966). "Accuracy and order of report in tachistoscopic recognition." Canadian Journal of Psychology, 20, 262-272.

Bryden, M. (1980). "Sex differences in brain organization: Different brains or different strategies?" Behavioral and Brain Sciences, 3, 230-231.

Bryden, M. (1982). Laterality. New York: Academic Press.

Bryden, M. & Allard, F. (1976). "Visual hemifield differences depend on typeface." Brain and Language, 3, 191-200.

Caramazza, A., Yeni-Komshian, G., Zurif, E. & Carbone, E. (1973). "The acquisition of a new phonological contrast: The case of stop consonants in French-English bilinguals." Journal of the Acoustical Society of America, 54, 421-428.

Carroll, F. (1980). "Neurolinguistic processing in bilingualism and second language." Research in Second Language Acquisition. Eds. R. Scarcella & S. Krashen. Rowley, MA.: Newbury House, 81-88.

Carter, R., Hohenegger, M. & Satz, P. (1980). "Handedness and aphasia: An inferential method for determining the mode of cerebral speech specialization." Neuropsychologia, 18, 569-574.

Cermak, L. & Craik, F. (Eds.) (1979). Levels of Processing in Human Memory. Hillsdale, N.J.: Lawrence Erlbaum Associates.

Charlton, M. (1964). "Aphasia in bilingual and polyglot patients - a neurological and psychological study." Journal of Speech and Hearing Disorders, 29, 307-311.

Clark, H. (1973). "The language-as-a-fixed-effect fallacy: A critique of language statistics in psychological research." Journal of Verbal Learning and Verbal Behavior, 12, 335-359.

Clark, H. & Clark, E. (1977). Psychology and Language: An Introduction to Psycholinguistics. New York: Harcourt Brace Jovanovich.

Clark, L. & Knowles, J. (1973). "Age differences in dichotic listening performance." Journal of Gerontology, 28, 173-178.

Cohen, G. (1973). "Hemispheric differences in serial versus parallel processing." Journal of Experimental Psychology, 97, 349-356.

Cohen, G. & Martin, M. (1975). "Hemisphere differences
    in an auditory Stroop test." <u>Perception and Psycho-</u>
    <u>physics</u>, 17, 79-83.

Colbourn, C. (1978). "Can laterality be measured?"
    <u>Neuropsychologia</u>, 16, 283-289.

Corballis, M. (1983). <u>Human Laterality</u>. New York: Academic
    Press.

Coren, S. & Porac, C. (1977). "Fifty centuries of right-
    handedness: The historical record." <u>Science</u>, 198,
    631-632.

Cornsweet, T. (1970). <u>Visual Perception</u>. New York:
    Academic Press.

Coulter, L. (1981). <u>Brain Lateralization for Reading in</u>
    <u>Arabic-English Bilinguals: A Tachistoscopic Study</u>.
    MA Thesis. American University, Cairo.

Craik, F. & Lockhart, R. (1972). "Levels of processing:
    A framework for memory research." <u>Journal of Verbal</u>
    <u>Learning and Verbal Behavior</u>, 11, 671-684.

Craik, F. & Tulving, E. (1975). "Depth of processing and
    the retention of words in episodic memory." <u>Journal</u>
    <u>of Experimental Psychology: General</u>, 104, 268-294.

Critchley, M. (1970). <u>Aphasiology and Other Aspects of</u>
    <u>Language</u>. London: Arnold.

Critchley, M. (1974). "Aphasia in polyglots and bilinguals."
    <u>Brain and Language</u>, 1, 15-27.

Curry, F. (1967). "A comparison of left-handed and right-
    handed subjects on verbal and nonverbal listening tasks."
    <u>Cortex</u>, 3, 343-352.

Davis, B. & Wertheimer, M. (1967). "Some determinants of
    associations to French and English words." <u>Journal of</u>
    <u>Verbal Learning and Verbal Behavior</u>, 6, 574-581.

Diller, K. (1974). "Compound and coordinate bilingualism:
    A conceptual artifact." <u>Word</u>, 26, 254-261.

Dingwall, W. & Whitaker, H. (1974). "Neurolinguistics."
    <u>Annual Review of Anthropology</u>, 3, 323-356.

REFERENCES

Dommergues, J. & Lane, H. (1976). "On two independent sources of error in learning the syntax of a second language." Language Learning, 26, 111-123.

Doob, L. (1957). "The effect of language on verbal expression and recall." American Anthropology, 59, 88-100.

Duškova, L. (1969). "On sources of error in foreign language learning." International Review of Applied Linguistics, 4, 11-36.

Dyer, F. (1973). "Interference and facilitation for color naming with separate bilateral presentation of the word and color." Journal of Experimental Psychology, 99, 314-377.

Ellegård, A. (1982). Språket och hjärnan. Enskede: Hammarström & Åberg.

Endo, M., Shimizu, A. & Nakamura, I. (1981a). "Laterality differences in recognition of Japanese and Hangul words by monolinguals and bilinguals." Cortex, 17, 381-400.

Endo, M., Shimizu, A. & Nakamura, I. (1981b). "The influence of Hangul learning upon laterality differences in Hangul word recognition by native Japanese subjects." Brain and Language, 14, 114-119.

Ervin, S. (1961). "Learning and recall in bilinguals." American Journal of Psychology, 74, 446-451.

Ervin, S. & Osgood, C. (1954). "Psycholinguistics: A survey of theory and research problems." Psycholinguistics. Eds. C. Osgood & T. Sebeok. Baltimore: Waverly Press, 139-146.

Ervin-Tripp, S. (1968). "An analysis of the interaction of language, topic, and listener." Readings in the Sociology of Language. Ed. J. Fishman. The Hague: Mouton.

Fairweather, H. (1976). "Sex differences in cognition." Cognition, 4, 231-280.

Galloway, L. (1977). The Brain and the Bilingual. Unpublished study. University of California, Los Angeles.

Galloway, L. (1980). "The convolutions of second language:
A theoretical article with a critical review and some
new hypotheses towards a neuropsychological model of
bilingualism and second language performance."
Language Learning, 31, 439-464.

Galloway, L. (1983). "The neuropsychology of bilingualism:
Theoretical considerations and a comprehensive review
of experimental and clinical research." Langages, 72,
79-123.

Galloway, L. & Gottfried, N. (1982). "Towards a neuropsychological model of verbal and non-verbal communication: Lesion evidence from bilingual aphasia for right
hemisphere participation in language." Forthcoming.

Galloway, L. & Scarcella, R. (1982). "Cerebral organization
in adult second language acquisition: Is the right
hemisphere more involved?" Brain and Language, 16,
56-60.

Gaziel, T., Obler, L. & Albert, M. (1978). "A tachisto-
scopic study of Hebrew-English bilinguals." The
Bilingual Brain. By M. Albert & L. Obler. New York:
Academic Press, 167-193.

Gekoski, W. (1969). "Associative and translation habits
of bilinguals as a function of language acquisition
context." Dissertation Abstracts, University of
Michigan, 30, 404-405.

Gekoski, W. (1970). "Effects of language acquisition
contexts on semantic processing in bilinguals."
Proceedings of the Annual Convention of the American
Psychological Association, 5, 487-488.

Genesee, F. (1982). "Experimental neuropsychological
research on second language processing." TESOL
Quarterly, 16, 315-322.

Genesee, F., Hamers, J., Lambert, W., Mononen, L., Seitz,
M. & Starck, R. (1978). "Language processing in
bilinguals." Brain and Language, 5, 1-12.

REFERENCES

Geschwind, N. & Levitsky, W. (1968). "Human brain: Left-right asymmetries in temporal speech region." Science, 161, 186-187.

Glanzer, M. & Duarte, A. (1971). "Repetition between and within languages in free recall." Journal of Verbal Learning and Verbal Behavior, 10, 625-630.

Gloning, I. & Gloning, K. (1965). "Aphasie bei Polyglotten: Beitrag zur Dynamik des Sprachbaus sowie zur Lokalizationsfrage dieser Störungen." Wiener Zeitschrift für Nervenheilkunde, 22, 363-397.

Goggin, J. & Wickens, D. (1971). "Proactive interference and language change in short-term memory." Journal of Verbal Learning and Verbal Behavior, 10, 435-458.

Goldstein, K. (1948). Language and Language Disturbances. New York: Grune and Stratton.

Gordon, H. (1980). "Cerebral organization in bilinguals." Brain and Language, 9, 255-268.

Gordon, H. & Carmon, A. (1976). "Transfer of dominance in speed of verbal response to visually presented stimuli from right to left hemispheres." Perceptual and Motor Skills, 42, 1091-1100.

Hamers, J. & Lambert, W. (1972). "Bilingual interdependencies in auditory perception." Journal of Verbal Learning and Verbal Behavior, 11, 303-310.

Hamers, J. & Lambert, W. (1977). "Visual field and cerebral hemisphere preferences in bilinguals." Language Development and Neurological Theory. Eds. S. Segalowitz & F. Gruber. New York: Academic Press, 59-63.

Harcum, E. & Finkel, M. (1963). "Explanation of Mishkin and Forgays' result as a directional reading conflict." Canadian Journal of Psychology, 17, 224-234.

Hardyck, C. (1977). "A model of individual differences in hemispheric functioning." Studies in Neurolinguistics, 3. Eds. H. Whitaker & H. Whitaker. New York: Academic Press, 223-255.

Hardyck, C., Tzeng, O. & Wang, S. (1977). "Cerebral
    lateralization effects in visual half-field experi-
    ments." Nature, 269, 705-707.

Hardyck, C., Tzeng, O. & Wang, S. (1978). "Cerebral
    lateralization of function and bilingual decision
    processes: Is thinking lateralized?" Brain and
    Language, 5, 56-71.

Harris, L. (1980). "Which hand is the 'eye' of the blind?
    A new look at an old question." Neuropsychology of
    Left Handedness. Ed. J. Herron. New York: Academic
    Press.

Hatch, E. (1977). "Second language learning." Bilingual
    Education: Current Perspectives, 2. Arlington, VA.:
    Center for Applied Linguistics, 60-86.

Hatta, T. (1978). "Recognition of Kanji and Hirakana in
    the left and right visual fields." Japanese Psycho-
    logical Research, 20, 51-59.

Hécaen, H. (1969). "Cerebral localization of mental
    functions and their disorders." Handbook of Clinical
    Neurology. Eds. P. Vinken & G. Bruyn. Amsterdam:
    North-Holland, 11-21.

Hécaen, H., De Agostini, M. & Monzon-Montes, A. (1981).
    "Cerebral organization in left-handers." Brain and
    Language, 12, 261-284.

Heron, W. (1957). "Perception as a function of retinal
    locus and attention." American Journal of Psychology,
    70, 38-48.

Hines, D. (1976). "Recognition of verbs, abstract nouns
    and concrete nouns from the left and right visual
    half-fields." Neuropsychologia, 14, 211-216.

Hines, D. (1977). "Differences in tachistoscopic recogni-
    tion between abstract and concrete words as a function
    of visual half-field and frequency." Cortex, 13, 66-73.

Hines, D. & Satz, P. (1974). "Cross-modal asymmetries in
    perception related to asymmetry in cerebral function."
    Neuropsychologia, 12, 239-247.

Huang, Y. & Jones, B. (1980). "Naming and discrimination of Chinese ideograms presented in the right and left visual fields." Neuropsychologia, 18, 703-706.

Hyde, T. & Jenkins, J. (1973). "Recall of words as a function of semantic, graphic, and syntactic orienting tasks." Journal of Verbal Learning and Verbal Behavior, 12, 471-480.

Hynd, G. & Scott, S. (1980). "Propositional and appositional modes of thought and differential speech lateralization in Navajo Indian and Anglo children." Child Development, 51, 909-917.

Ingvar, D. (1983). "Serial aspects of language and speech related to prefrontal cortical activity." Human Neurobiology, 2, 177-189.

Jacobovitz, L. & Lambert, W. (1961). "Semantic satiation among bilinguals." Journal of Experimental Psychology, 62, 576-582.

Kaplan, C. & TenHouten, W. (1975). "Neurolinguistic sociology." Sociolinguists' Newsletter, 6, 4-9.

Keppel, G. (1973). Design and Analysis: A Researcher's Handbook. Englewood Cliffs, N.J.: Prentice-Hall.

Kershner, J. & Jeng, A. (1972). "Dual functional hemispheric asymmetry in visual perception: Effects of ocular dominance and postexposural processes." Neuropsychologia, 10, 437-445.

Kimura, D. (1961a). "Cerebral dominance and the perception of verbal stimuli." Canadian Journal of Psychology, 15, 166-171.

Kimura, D. (1961b). "Some effects of temporal lobe damage on auditory perception." Canadian Journal of Psychology, 15, 156-165.

Kimura, D. (1966). "Dual functional asymmetry of the brain in visual perception." Neuropsychologia, 4, 275-285.

Kimura, D. (1973). "The asymmetry of the human brain." Scientific American, 228, 70-78.

Kimura, D. (1980). "Sex differences in intrahemispheric organization of speech." Behavioral and Brain Sciences, 3, 240-241.

Kimura, D. (1983). "Sex differences in cerebral organization for speech and praxic functions." Canadian Journal of Psychology, 37, 19-35.

Kinsbourne, M. (1970). "The cerebral basis of lateral asymmetries in attention." Acta Psychologia, 33, 193-201.

Kinsbourne, M. & Hiscock, M. (1977). "Does cerebral dominance develop?" Language Development and Neurological Theory. Eds. S. Segalowitz & F. Gruber. New York: Academic Press.

Kintsch, W. (1977). Memory and Cognition. New York: John Wiley.

Kintsch, W. & Kintsch, E. (1969). "Interlingual interference and memory processes." Journal of Verbal Learning and Verbal Behavior, 8, 16-19.

Kolers, P. (1963). "Interlingual word associations." Journal of Verbal Learning and Verbal Behavior, 2, 291-300.

Kolers, P. (1966). "Reading and talking bilingually." American Journal of Psychology, 79, 357-376.

Kolers, P. & Gonzalez, E. (1980). "Memory for words, synonyms, and translations." Journal of Experimental Psychology: Human Learning and Memory, 6, 53-65.

Kotik, B. (1975). "A dichotic listening study with Russian-Estonian bilinguals." An Investigation of Interhemispheric Auditory Information Processing. Thesis for the Kandidat degree. Moscow State University.

Krashen, S. (1973). "Lateralization, language learning, and the critical period: Some new evidence." Language Learning, 23, 63-74.

Krashen, S. (1981). Second Language Acquisition and Second Language Learning. Oxford: Pergamon Press.

Krashen, S. & Galloway, L. (1978). "The neurological

correlates of language acquisition." <u>SPEAQ Journal</u>, 2, 21-35.

Kroll, J. & Potter, M. (1984). "Recognizing words, pictures, and concepts: A comparison of lexical, object, and reality decisions." <u>Journal of Verbal Learning and Verbal Behavior</u>, 23, 39-66.

Kučera, H. & Francis, W. (1967). <u>Computational Analysis of Present-Day American English</u>. Providence, R.I.: Brown University Press.

Lake, D. & Bryden, M. (1976). "Handedness in hemispheric asymmetry." <u>Brain and Language</u>, 3, 266-282.

Lambert, W. (1969). "Psychological studies of the inter-dependencies of the bilingual's two languages." <u>Substance and Structure of Language</u>. Ed. J. Puhvel. Berkeley: University of California Press, 99-125.

Lambert, W., Havelka, J. & Crosby, D. (1958). "The influence of language-acquisition contexts on bi-lingualism." <u>Journal of Abnormal and Social Psychology</u>, 56, 239-243.

Lambert, W. & Fillenbaum, S. (1959). "A pilot study of aphasia among bilinguals." <u>Canadian Journal of Psychology</u>, 13, 28-34.

Lambert, W. & Preston, M. (1967). "The interdependencies of the bilingual's two languages." <u>Research on Verbal Behavior and Some Neurological Implications</u>. Eds. K. Salzinger & S. Salzinger. New York: Academic Press, 115-120.

Lambert, W., Ignatow, M. & Krauthammer, M. (1968). "Bilingual organization in free recall." <u>Journal of Verbal Learning and Verbal Behavior</u>, 7, 207-214.

Lambert, W. & Rawlings, C. (1969). "Bilingual processing of mixed-language associative networks." <u>Journal of Verbal Learning and Verbal Behavior</u>, 8, 604-609.

Lamendella, J. (1977). "General principles of neuro-functional organization and their manifestation in primary and nonprimary language acquisition."

Language Learning, 27, 155-196.

Lansdell, H. (1962). "A sex difference in effect of temporal lobe neurosurgery on design preference." _Nature_, 194, 852-854.

LeMay, M. & Culebras, A. (1972). "Human brain-morphological differences in the hemispheres demonstrable by carotid angiography." _New England Journal of Medicine_, 287, 168-170.

Lenneberg, E. (1967). _Biological Foundations of Language_. New York: John Wiley.

Levy, J. (1974). "Psychobiological implications of bi-lateral asymmetry." _Hemisphere Function in the Human Brain_. Eds. S. Diamond & J. Beaumont. New York: Halstead Press.

Levy, J., Trevarthen, C. & Sperry, R. (1972). "Perception of bilateral chimeric figures following hemispheric deconnexion." _Brain_, 95, 61-78.

Levy-Agresti, J. & Sperry, R. (1968). "Differential perceptual capacities in major and minor hemispheres." _Proceedings of the National Academy of Sciences_, 61, 115.

L'Hermitte, R., Hécaen, H., Dubois, J., Culioli, A. & Tabouret-Keller, A. (1966). "Le probleme de l'aphasie des polyglottes: Remarques sur quelques observations." _Neuropsychologia_, 4, 315-329.

LoCoco, V. (1975). "An analysis of Spanish and German learners' errors." _Working Papers on Bilingualism_, 7, 96-124.

Lopez, M. & Young, R. (1974). "The linguistic inter-dependence of bilinguals." _Journal of Experimental Psychology_, 6, 981-983.

Luria, A. (1960). "Differences between disturbance of speech and writing in Russian and French." _International Journal of Slavic Linguistics and Poetics_, 3, 13-22.

Luria, A. (1970). _Traumatic Aphasia_. The Hague: Mouton.

Maccoby, E. & Jacklin, C. (1974). _The Psychology of Sex Differences_. Stanford: Stanford University Press.

REFERENCES

MacKay, D. (1976). "On the retrieval and lexical structure
of verbs." Journal of Verbal Learning and Verbal
Behavior, 15, 169-182.

MacKay, D. & Bowman, R. (1969). "On producing the meaning
in sentences." American Journal of Psychology, 82,
23-39.

Macnamara, J. (1966). Bilingualism and Primary Education.
Edinburgh, Scotland: Edinburgh University Press.

Macnamara, J. (1970). "Comparative studies of reading and
problem-solving in two languages." TESOL Quarterly, 4,
107-116.

Macnamara, J. & Kushnir, S. (1971). "Linguistic independence of bilinguals: The input switch." Journal
of Verbal Learning and Verbal Behavior, 10, 480-487.

Maitre, S. (1974). On the Representation of Second
Language in the Brain. MA Thesis. University of
California, Los Angeles.

Marshall, J., Caplan, D. & Holmes, J. (1975). "The
measure of laterality." Neuropsychologia, 13, 315-321.

McCormack, P. (1977). "Bilingual linguistic memory: The
independence-interdependence issue revisited."
Bilingualism: Psychological, Social, and Educational
Implications. Ed. P. Hornby. New York: Academic Press,
57-66.

McGlone, J. (1980). "Sex differences in human brain
asymmetry: A critical survey." Behavioral and Brain
Sciences, 3, 215-263.

McKeever, W. (1981). "On laterality research and dichotomania." Behavioral and Brain Sciences, 4, 73-74.

McLaughlin, B. (1978). Second Language Acquisition in
Childhood. Hillsdale, N.J.: Lawrence Erlbaum Associates.

Miller, G. (1956). "The magical number seven, plus or
minus two: Some limits on our capacity for processing
information." Psychological Review, 63, 81-97.

Milner, B. (1975). "Psychological aspects of focal epilepsy
and its neurosurgical management." Advances in Neurology,

8. Eds. D. Purpura, J. Penry & R. Walters. New York:
Raven.

Mishkin, N. & Forgays, D. (1952). "Word recognition as a
function of retinal locus." Journal of Experimental
Psychology, 43, 43-48.

Mononen, L. & Seitz, M. (1977). "An AER analysis of contralateral advantage in the transmission of auditory information." Neuropsychologia, 15, 165-174.

Nair, K. & Virmani, V. (1973). "Speech and language
disturbances in hemiplegics." Indian Journal of Medical
Research, 61, 1395-1403.

Nas, G. (1983). "Visual word recognition in bilinguals:
Evidence for a cooperation between visual and sound
based codes during access to a common lexical store."
Journal of Verbal Learning and Verbal Behavior, 22,
526-534.

Neufeld, G. (1976). "The bilingual's lexical store."
IRAL, 14, 15-35.

Nordlund, G. (1975). Prognos av Framgång i Gymnasieskolan:
Metodproblem och Empiriska Resultat. Akademisk av-
handling. Umeå Universitet.

Norrsell, U. (1985). Hjärnstrukturer och Språkfunktion.
Paper presented at the TLH Symposium, Göteborg.

Obler, L. (1981). The Neuropsychology of Bilingualism.
Paper presented at the Biological Perspectives on
Language Symposium, Montreal.

Obler, L., Albert, M. & Gordon, H. (1975). Asymmetry of
Cerebral Dominance in Hebrew-English Bilinguals. Paper
presented at the Thirteenth Annual Meeting of the
Academy of Aphasia, Victoria, B.C.

Obler, L. & Albert, M. (1978). "A monitor system for
bilingual language processing." Aspects of Bilingualism.
Ed. M. Paradis. Colombia, S.C.: Hornbeam Press, 156-164.

Obler, L., Zatorre, R., Galloway, L. & Vaid, J. (1982).
"Cerebral lateralization in bilinguals: Methodological
issues." Brain and Language, 15, 40-54.

REFERENCES

Ojemann, G. & Whitaker, H. (1978). "The bilingual brain." <u>Archives of Neurology</u>, 35, 409–412.

Oldfield, R. (1971). "The assessment and analysis of handedness: The Edinburgh Inventory." <u>Neuropsychologia</u>, 9, 97–114.

Olton, R. (1960). <u>Semantic Generalization between Languages</u>. Unpublished MA Thesis. McGill University.

Orbach, J. (1967). "Differential recognition of Hebrew and English words in right and left visual fields as a function of cerebral dominance and reading habits." <u>Neuropsychologia</u>, 5, 127–134.

Ovcharova, P., Raichev, R. & Geleva, T. (1968). "Afeziya u poligloti." <u>Neurohirurgiia</u>, 7, 183–190.

Overton, W. & Wiener, M. (1966). "Visual field position and word recognition threshold." <u>Journal of Experimental Psychology</u>, 71, 249–253.

Paivio, A. & Begg, I. (1981). <u>Psychology of Language</u>. Englewood Cliffs, N.J.: Prentice-Hall.

Paivio, A. & Lambert, W. (1981). "Dual coding and bilingual memory." <u>Journal of Verbal Learning and Verbal Behavior</u>, 20, 532–539.

Paradis, M. (1977). "Bilingualism and aphasia." <u>Studies in Neurolinguistics</u>, 3. Eds. H. Whitaker & H. Whitaker. New York: Academic Press, 65–121.

Pellegrino, J., Rosinski, R., Chiesi, H. & Siegel, A. (1977). "Picture-word differences in decision latency: An analysis of single and dual memory models." <u>Memory and Cognition</u>, 5, 383–396.

Penfield, W. & Roberts, L. (1959). <u>Speech and Brain Mechanisms</u>. Princeton, N.J.: Princeton University Press.

Peuser, G. & Leischner, A. (1974). "Störungen der Phonetischen Schrift bei einem Aphasiker." <u>Neuropsychologia</u>, 12, 557–560.

Piazza, D. & Zatorre, R. (1981). "A right-ear advantage for dichotic listening in bilingual children." <u>Brain and Language</u>, 13, 389–396.

Poetzl, O. (1930). "Aphasie und Mehrsprachigkeit."
Zeitschrift für die gesamte Neurologie und Psychiatrie,
124, 145-162.

Potter, M. & Faulconer, B. (1975). "Time to understand
pictures and words." Nature, 253, 437-438.

Potter, M., So, K., von Eckardt, B. & Feldman, L. (1984).
"Lexical and conceptual representation in beginning and
proficient bilinguals." Journal of Verbal Learning and
Verbal Behavior, 23, 23-28.

Preston, M. & Lambert, W. (1969). "Interlingual interference in a bilingual version of the Stroop color-word
task." Journal of Verbal Learning and Verbal Behavior,
8, 295-301.

Rapport, R., Tan, C. & Whitaker, H. (1980). Language
Function and Dysfunction among Chinese Polyglots.
Paper presented at Academy of Aphasia, Fall River, MA.

Rasmussen, T. & Milner, B. (1977). "The role of early
left-brain injury in determining lateralization of
cerebral speech functions." Annals of the New York
Academy of Science, 299, 355-369.

Riegel, K. (1968). "Some theoretical considerations of
bilingual duplication." Psychological Bulletin, 70,
647-670.

Rife, D. (1951). "Heredity and handedness." Scientific
Monthly, 73, 188-191.

Rogers, L., TenHouten, W., Kaplan, C. & Gardiner, M.
(1977). "Hemispheric specialization of language:
An EEG study of bilingual Hopi Indian children."
International Journal of Neuroscience, 8, 1-6.

Rosansky, E. (1975). "The critical period for the acquisition of language: Some cognitive developmental
considerations." Working Papers on Bilingualism,
6, 92-102.

Rose, R., Rose, P., King, N. & Perez, A. (1975). "Bilingual
memory for related and unrelated sentences." Journal of
Experimental Psychology, 1, 599-606.

REFERENCES

Sasanuma, S. (1974). "Kanji versus Kana processing in
   alexia with transient agraphia: A case report."
   Cortex, 10, 89-97.

Sasanuma, S., Itoh, M., Kobayashi, Y. & Mori, K. (1980).
   "The nature of the task-stimulus interaction in the
   tachistoscopic recognition of Kana and Kanji words."
   Brain and Language, 9, 298-306.

Satz, P. (1968). "Laterality effects in dichotic listening."
   Nature, 218, 277-288.

Satz, P., Achenbach, K., Pattishall, E. & Fennel, E. (1965).
   "Order of report, ear asymmetry, and handedness in
   dichotic listening." Cortex, 1, 377-396.

Scarborough, D., Gerard, L. & Cortese, C. (1984).
   "Independence of lexical access in bilingual word
   recognition." Journal of Verbal Learning and Verbal
   Behavior, 23, 84-99.

Schneiderman, E. & Wesche, M. (1983). "Right hemisphere
   participation in second language acquisition." Issues
   in Second Language Acquisition: Selected Papers of
   the Los Angeles Second Language Research Forum.
   Eds. K. Bailey, M. Long & S. Peck. Rowley, MA.:
   Newbury House.

Scholes, R. (1968). "Phonemic interference as a perceptual
   phenomenon." Language and Speech, 11, 86-103.

Scott, S., Hynd, G., Hunt, L. & Weed, W. (1979). "Cerebral
   speech lateralization in the native American Navajo."
   Neuropsychologia, 17, 89-92.

Searleman, A. (1977). "A review of right hemisphere
   linguistic capabilities." Psychological Bulletin, 84,
   503-528.

Segalowitz, N. & Lambert, W. (1969). "Semantic generalization in bilinguals." Journal of Verbal Learning and
   Verbal Behavior, 8, 559-566.

Shimizu, A. & Endo, M. (1981). "Tachistoscopic recognition
   of Kana and Hangul words, handedness and shift of
   laterality difference." Neuropsychologia, 19, 665-673.

Silverberg, R., Bentin, S., Gaziel, L., Obler, L. & Albert, M. (1979). "Shift of visual field preference for English words in native Hebrew speakers." Brain and Language, 8, 184-190.

Stafford, K. (1968). "Problem solving as a function of language." Language and Speech, 11, 104-112.

Studdert-Kennedy, M. (1975). "Dichotic studies II: Two questions." Brain and Language, 2, 123-130.

Studdert-Kennedy, M. (1981). "Cerebral hemispheres: Specialized for the analysis of what?" Behavioral and Brain Sciences, 4, 76-77.

Sussman, H., Franklin, P. & Simon, T. (1980). Bilingual Speech: Bilateral Control? Unpublished manuscript. University of Texas, Austin.

Taylor, I. (1971). "How are words from two languages organized in bilinguals' memory?" Canadian Journal of Psychology, 25, 228-240.

Taylor, I. (1976a). Introduction to Psycholinguistics. New York: Holt, Rinehart and Winston.

Taylor, I. (1976b). "Similarity between French and English words - a factor to be considered in bilingual behavior?" Journal of Psycholinguistic Research, 5, 85-94.

Taylor, J. (Ed.) (1958). Selected Writings of John Hughlings Jackson, 2. London: Staples.

Tomlinson-Keasey, C. & Kelly, R. (1979). "A task analysis of hemispheric functioning." Neuropsychologia, 17, 345-351.

Tsao, Y., Feutsel, T. & Soesos, C. (1979). "Stroop interference in the left and right visual fields." Brain and Language, 8, 367-371.

Tsao, Y., Wu, M. & Feutsel, T. (1981). "Stroop interference: Hemispheric difference in Chinese speakers." Brain and Language, 13, 372-378.

Tulving, E. & Colotla, V. (1970). "Free recall of trilingual lists." Cognitive Psychology, 1, 86-98.

224   REFERENCES

Vaid, J. (1981). <u>Tachistoscopic Stroop Study: Hindi and</u>
    <u>Urdu</u>. South Asian Languages Round Table. Story Brook,
    New York.

Vaid, J. & Lambert, W. (1979). "Differential cerebral
    involvement in the cognitive functioning of bilinguals."
    <u>Brain and Language</u>, 8, 92-110.

Vaid, J. & Genesee, F. (1980). "Neuropsychological
    approaches to bilingualism." <u>Canadian Journal of</u>
    <u>Psychology</u>, 34, 417-445.

Vernon, P. (1960). <u>Intelligence and Attainment Tests</u>.
    London: University of London Press.

Vildomec, V. (1963). <u>Multilingualism</u>. Leyden: A.W.
    Sythoff.

Waber, D. (1977). "Sex differences in mental abilities,
    hemisphere lateralization, and rate of physical growth
    at adolescence." <u>Developmental Psychology</u>, 13, 29-38.

Wada, J. & Rasmussen, T. (1960). "Intracarotid injection
    of sodium amytal for the lateralization of cerebral
    speech dominance: Experimental and clinical observa-
    tions." <u>Journal of Neurosurgery</u>, 17, 266-282.

Wada, J., Clarke, R. & Hamm, A. (1975). "Cerebral hemi-
    spheric asymmetry in humans." <u>Archives of Neurology</u>,
    32, 239-246.

Walters, J. & Zatorre, R. (1978). "Laterality differences
    for word identification in bilinguals." <u>Brain and</u>
    <u>Language</u>, 2, 158-167.

Warrington, E. & Pratt, R. (1973). "Language laterality
    in left handers assessed by unilateral E.C.T."
    <u>Neuropsychologia</u>, 11, 423-428.

Watamori, T. & Sasanuma, S. (1978). "The recovery process
    of two English-Japanese bilingual aphasics." <u>Brain and</u>
    <u>Language</u>, 6, 127-140.

Waugh, N. & Norman, D. (1965). "Primary memory." <u>Psycho-</u>
    <u>logical Review</u>, 72, 89-104.

Wesche, M. & Schneiderman, E. (1981). <u>Language Lateraliza-</u>
    <u>tion in Adult Bilinguals</u>. Sixth World Congress of the

International Association of Applied Linguistics, Sweden.

Weinreich, U. (1953). Languages in Contact – Findings and Problems. New York: Linguistic Circle.

Whitaker, H. (1978). "Bilingualism: A neurolinguistics perspective." Second Language Acquisition. Ed. W. Ritchie. New York: Academic Press, 21-32.

White, M. (1973). "Does cerebral dominance offer a sufficient explanation for laterality differences in tachistoscopic recognition?" Perceptual and Motor Skills, 20, 479-485.

Wike, E. & Church, J. (1976). "Comments on Clark's 'The language-as-a-fixed-effect fallacy'." Journal of Verbal Learning and Verbal Behavior, 15, 249-255.

Witelson, S. (1977). "Early hemisphere specialization and interhemispheric plasticity." Language Development and Neurological Theory. Eds. S. Segalowitz & F. Gruber. New York: Academic Press, 213-287.

Witelson, S. & Pallie, W. (1973). "Left hemisphere specialization for language in the newborn." Brain, 96, 641-646.

Wolf, E. & Gardiner, J. (1963). "Sensitivity of the retinal area in one eye corresponding to the blind spot in the other eye." Journal of the Optical Society of America, 53, 1437-1440.

Wyke, M. & Chorover, S. (1965). "Comparison of spatial discrimination in the temporal and nasal sectors of the monocular visual field." Perceptual and Motor Skills, 20, 1037-1045.

Zaidel, E. (1976). "Auditory vocabulary of the right hemisphere following brain bisection or hemidecortication." Cortex, 12, 191-211.

Zaidel, E. (1978). "Lexical organization in the right hemisphere." Cerebral Correlates of Conscious Experience. Eds. P. Buser & A. Rougeul-Buser. Amsterdam: Elsevier/ North-Holland.

REFERENCES

Zangwill, O. (1960). <u>Cerebral Dominance and its Relations to Psychological Function</u>. Edinburgh: Oliver and Boyd.

Zangwill, O. (1967). "Speech and the minor hemisphere." <u>Acta Neurologica et Psychiatrica Belgiica</u>, 67, 1013–1020.

Zurif, E. & Bryden, M. (1969). "Familial handedness and left-right differences in auditory and visual perception." <u>Neuropsychologia</u>, 7, 179–188.